ARE **4.0**

2010

Building Systems

Questions & Answers   John Hardt

KAPLAN

AE EDUCATION

President: Dr. Andrew Temte

Chief Learning Officer: Dr. Tim Smaby

Vice President of Engineering Education: Dr. Jeffrey Manzi, PE

Senior Product Manager: Brian O'Connor

BUILDING SYSTEMS QUESTIONS & ANSWERS: 2010 EDITION

© 1995 by Architectural License Seminars, Inc.

© 2009 by Dearborn Financial Publishing, Inc.®

Published by Kaplan Architecture Education

1905 Palace Street

La Crosse, WI 54603

800-420-1429

www.kaplanarchitecture.com

Printed in the United States of America.

09   10   11   10 9 8 7 6 5 4 3 2 1

ISBN: 1-4277-8670-4
PPN: 1629-3202

CONTENTS

WELCOME

Thank you for choosing Kaplan AE Education for your ARE study needs. We offer updates annually to keep abreast of code and exam changes and to address any errors discovered since the previous update was published. We wish you the best of luck in your pursuit of licensure.

ARE OVERVIEW

Since the State of Illinois first pioneered the practice of licensing architects in 1897, architectural licensing has been increasingly adopted as a means to protect the public health, safety, and welfare. Today, the United States and Canadian provinces require licensing for individuals practicing architecture. Licensing requirements vary by jurisdiction; however, the minimum requirements are uniform and in all cases include passing the Architect Registration Examination (ARE). This makes the ARE a required rite of passage for all those entering the profession, and you should be congratulated on undertaking this challenging endeavor.

Developed by the National Council of Architectural Registration Boards (NCARB), the ARE is the only exam by which architecture candidates can become registered in the United States or Canada. The ARE assesses candidates' knowledge, skills, and abilities in seven different areas of professional practice, including a candidate's competency in decision making and knowledge of various areas of the profession. The exam also tests competence in fulfilling an architect's responsibilities and in coordinating the activities of others while working with a team of design and construction specialists. In all jurisdictions, candidates must pass the seven divisions of the exam to become registered.

The ARE is designed and prepared by architects, making it a practice-based exam. It is generally not a test of academic knowledge, but rather a means to test decision-making ability as it relates to the responsibilities of the architectural profession. For example, the exam does not expect candidates to memorize specific details of the building code, but requires them to understand a model code's general requirements, scope, and purpose, and to know the architect's responsibilities related to that code. As such, there is no substitute for a well-rounded internship to help prepare for the ARE.

4.0 Exam Format

The seven ARE 4.0 divisions are outlined in the table below.

DIVISION	QUESTIONS	VIGNETTES
Building Design & Construction Systems	85	Accessibility/ Ramp Roof Plan Stair Design
Building Systems	95	Mechanical & Electrical Plan
Construction Documents & Services	100	Building Section
Programming, Planning & Practice	85	Site Zoning
Schematic Design	-	Building Layout Interior Layout
Site Planning & Design	65	Site Design Site Grading
Structural Systems	125	Structural Layout

The exam presents multiple-choice questions individually. Candidates may answer questions, skip questions, or mark questions for further review. Candidates may also move backward or forward within the exam using

ARCHITECTURAL HISTORY

Questions pertaining to the history of architecture appear throughout the ARE. The prominence of historical questions will vary not only by division but also within different versions of the exam for each division. In general, however, history tends to be lightly tested, with approximately three to seven history questions per division, depending upon the total number of questions within the division. One aspect common to all the divisions is that whatever history questions are presented will be related to that division's subject matter. For example, a question regarding Chicago's John Hancock Center and the purpose of its unique exterior cross bracing may appear on the Structural Systems exam.

Though it is difficult to predict how essential your knowledge of architectural history will be to passing any of the multiple-choice divisions, it is recommended that you refer to a primer in this field—such as Kaplan's *Architectural History*—before taking each exam, and that you keep an eye out for topics relevant to the division for which you are studying. It is always better to be overprepared than taken by surprise at the testing center.

simple on-screen icons. The vignettes require candidates to create a graphic solution according to program and code requirements.

Actual appointment times for taking the exam are slightly longer than the actual exam time, allowing candidates to check in and out of the testing center. All ARE candidates are encouraged to review NCARB's *ARE Guidelines* for further detail about the exam format. These guidelines are available via free download at NCARB's Web site (*www.ncarb.org*).

Exam Format

It is important for exam candidates to familiarize themselves not only with exam content, but also with question format. Familiarity with the basic question types found in the ARE will reduce confusion, save time, and help you pass the exam. The ARE contains three basic question types.

The first and most common type is a straightforward multiple-choice question followed by four choices (A, B, C, and D). Candidates are expected to select the correct answer. This type of question is shown in the following example.

Which of the following cities is the capital of the United States?

A. New York

B. Washington, D.C.

C. Chicago

D. Los Angeles

The second type of question is a negatively worded question. In questions such as this, the negative wording is usually highlighted using all caps, as shown below.

Which of the following cities is *NOT* located on the west coast of the United States?

A. Los Angeles

B. San Diego

C. San Francisco

D. New York

The third type of question is a combination question. In a combination question, more than one choice may be correct; candidates must select from combinations of potentially correct choices. An example of a combination question is shown on the following page.

Which of the following cities are located within the United States?

- **I.** New York
- **II.** Toronto
- **III.** Montreal
- **IV.** Los Angeles
- **A.** I only
- **B.** I and II
- **C.** II and III
- **D.** **I and IV**

The single most important thing candidates can do to prepare themselves for the vignettes is to learn to proficiently navigate NCARB's graphic software. Practice software can be downloaded free of charge from their Web site. Candidates should download it and become thoroughly familiar with its use.

Recommendations on Exam Division Order

NCARB allows candidates to choose the order in which they take the exams, and the choice is an important one. While only you know what works best for you, the following are some general considerations that many have found to be beneficial:

1. The Building Design & Construction Systems and Programming, Planning & Practice divisions are perhaps the broadest of all the divisions. Although this can make them among the most intimidating, taking these divisions early in the process will give a candidate a broad base of knowledge and may prove helpful in preparing for subsequent divisions. An alternative to this approach is to take these two divisions last, since you will already be familiar with much of their content. This latter approach likely is most beneficial when you take the exam divisions in fairly rapid succession so that details learned while studying for earlier divisions will still be fresh in your mind.

2. The Construction Documents & Services exam covers a broad range of subjects, dealing primarily with the architect's role and responsibilities within the building design and construction team. Because these subjects serve as one of the core foundations of the ARE, it may be advisable to take this division early in the process, as knowledge gained preparing for this exam can help in subsequent divisions.

3. Take exams that particularly concern you early in the process. NCARB rules prohibit retaking an exam for six months. Therefore, failing an exam early in the process will allow the candidate to use the waiting period to prepare for and take other exams.

EXAM PREPARATION

Overview

There is little argument that preparation is key to passing the ARE. With this in mind, Kaplan has developed a complete learning system for each exam division, including study guides, question-and-answer handbooks, mock exams, and flash cards. The study guides offer a condensed course of study and will best prepare you for the exam when utilized along with the other tools in the learning system. The system is designed to provide you with the general background necessary to pass the exam and to provide an indication of specific content areas that demand additional attention.

In addition to the Kaplan learning system, materials from industry-standard documents may prove useful for the various divisions. Several of these sources are noted in the "Supplementary Study Materials" section on page ix.

Understanding the Field

The subject of building systems rarely falls directly under the responsibility of the architect, but such systems are largely responsible for achieving the most basic objectives in architecture—health, safety, comfort, and convenience for occupants. The subject must be understood for architects to properly integrate these systems within their designs and to permit the architect to interact constructively with other members of the building design team.

Understanding the Exam

The building systems exam covers subjects including sustainability, plumbing systems, thermal protection systems, lighting, acoustics, mechanical, fire protection, and transportation systems. A basic understanding of the function and purpose of these systems is needed in order to succeed with this exam. However, the exam does not extensively test a candidate's knowledge of the detailed design of such systems, rather their components and how they function. Environmental and energy conservation is a major focus on the exam material. Further, candidates should possess knowledge of how plumbing affects health as well as life safety systems.

For the Mechanical and Electrical Plan vignette, remember to connect all HVAC diffusers to the main ductwork with flex duct—even if the diffuser is adjacent to or touches a rigid duct. Also, make sure that each space has enough light fixtures and diffusers to meet the program requirements.

Preparation Basics

The first step in preparation should be a review of the exam specifications and reference materials published by NCARB. These statements are available for each of the seven ARE divisions to serve as a guide for preparing for the exam. Download these statements and familiarize yourself with their content. This will help you focus your attention on the subjects on which the exam focuses.

Prior CAD knowledge is not necessary to successfully complete vignettes. In fact, it's important for candidates familiar with CAD to realize they will experience significant differences between CAD and the drawing tools used on the exam.

Though no two people will have exactly the same ARE experience, the following are recommended best practices to adopt in your studies and should serve as a guide.

Set aside scheduled study time.
Establish a routine and adopt study strategies that reflect your strengths and mirror your approach in other successful academic pursuits. Most importantly, set aside a definite amount of study time each week, just as if you were taking a lecture course, and carefully read all of the material.

Take—and retake—quizzes.
After studying each lesson in the study guide, take the quiz found at its conclusion. The quiz questions are intended to be straightforward and objective. Answers and explanations can be found at the back of the book. If you answer a question incorrectly, see if you can determine why the correct answer is correct before reading the explanation. Retake the quiz until you answer every question correctly and understand why the correct answers are correct.

Identify areas for improvement.
The quizzes allow you the opportunity to pinpoint areas where you need improvement. Reread and take note of the sections that cover these areas and seek additional information from other sources. Use the question-and-answer handbook and online test bank as a final tune-up for the exam.

Take the final exam.

A final exam designed to simulate the ARE follows the last lesson of each study guide. Answers and explanations can be found on the pages following the exam. As with the lesson quizzes, retake the final exam until you answer every question correctly and understand why the correct answers are correct.

Use the flash cards.

If you've purchased the flash cards, go through them once and set aside any terms you know at first glance. Take the rest to work, reviewing them on the train, over lunch, or before bed. Remove cards as you become familiar with their terms until you know all the terms. Review all the cards a final time before taking the exam.

Practice using the NCARB software.

Work through the practice vignettes contained within the NCARB software. You should work through each vignette repeatedly until you can solve it easily. As your skills develop, track how long it takes to work through a solution for each vignette.

Supplementary Study Materials

In addition to the Kaplan learning system, materials from industry-standard sources may prove useful in your studies. Candidates should consult the list of exam references in the NCARB guidelines for the council's recommendations and pay particular attention to the following publications, which are essential to successfully completing this exam:

- International Code Council (ICC) *International Building Code*

- *Standard on Accessible and Usable Buildings and Facilities* (ICC/ANSI A117.1-98)

- National Fire Protection Association *Life Safety Code* (NFPA 101)

- American Institute of Architects B141-1997 *Standard Form of Agreement Between Owner and Architect*

- American Institute of Architects A201-1997 *General Conditions of the Contract for Construction*

- American Institute of Steel Construction *Manual of Steel Construction: Allowable Stress Design*, Ninth Edition

Test-Taking Advice

Preparation for the exam should include a review of successful test-taking procedures—especially for those who have been out of the classroom for some time. Following is advice to aid in your success.

Pace yourself.

Each division allows candidates at least one minute per question. You should be able to comfortably read and reread each question and fully understand what is being asked before answering. Each vignette allows candidate ample time to complete a solution within the time allotted.

Read carefully.

Begin each question by reading it carefully and fully reviewing the choices, eliminating those that are obviously incorrect. Interpret language literally, and keep an eye out for negatively worded questions. With vignettes, carefully review instructions and requirements. Quickly make a list of program and code requirements to check your work against as you proceed through the vignette.

Guess.

All unanswered questions are considered incorrect, so answer every question. If you are unsure of the correct answer, select your best guess and/or mark the question for later review. If you continue to be unsure of the answer after returning to the question a second time, it is usually best to stick with your first guess.

Review difficult questions.

The exam allows candidates to review and change answers within the time limit. Utilize this feature to mark troubling questions for review upon completing the rest of the exam.

Reference material.

Some divisions include reference materials accessible through an on-screen icon. These materials include formulas and other reference content that may prove helpful when answering questions in these divisions. Note that candidates may not bring reference material with them to the testing center.

Best answer questions.

Many candidates fall victim to questions seeking the "best" answer. In these cases, it may appear at first glance as though several choices are correct. Remember the importance of reviewing the question carefully and interpreting the language literally. Consider the following example.

> Which of these cities is located on the east coast of the United States?
>
> **A.** Boston
> **B.** Philadelphia
> **C.** Washington, D.C.
> **D.** Atlanta

At first glance, it may appear that all of the cities could be correct answers. However, if you interpret the question literally, you'll identify the critical phrase as "on the east coast." Although each of the cities listed is arguably an "eastern" city, only Boston sits on the Atlantic coast. All the other choices are located in the eastern part of the country, but are not coastal cities.

Style doesn't count.

Vignettes are graded on their conformance with program requirements and instructions. Don't waste time creating aesthetically pleasing solutions and adding unnecessary design elements.

ACKNOWLEDGMENTS

This introduction was written by John F. Hardt, AIA. Mr. Hardt is vice president and senior project architect with Karlsberger, an architecture, planning, and design firm based in Columbus, Ohio. He is a graduate of Ohio State University (MArch).

ABOUT KAPLAN

Thank you for choosing Kaplan AE Education as your source for ARE preparation materials. Whether helping future professors prepare for the GRE or providing tomorrow's doctors the tools they need to pass the MCAT, Kaplan possesses more than 50 years of experience as a global leader in exam prep and educational publishing. It is that experience and history that Kaplan brings to the world of architectural education, pairing unparalleled resources with acknowledged experts in ARE content areas to bring you the very best in licensure study materials.

Only Kaplan AE offers a complete catalog of individual products and integrated learning systems to help you pass all seven divisions of the ARE. Kaplan's ARE materials include study guides, mock exams, question-and-answer handbooks, video workshops, and flash cards. Products may be purchased individually or in division-specific learning systems to suit your needs. These systems are designed to help you better focus on essential information for each division, provide flexibility in how you study, and save you money.

To order, please visit *www.kaplanarchitecture. com* or call 800-420-1429.

SYMBOLS & ABBREVIATIONS

The following symbols and abbreviations are used in this book and are generally understood in structural design practice.

Symbol or Abbreviation	Meaning
ft. or '	foot
ft^2 or sq. ft.	square foot
ft^3 or cu. ft.	cubic foot
ft.-kip or ft.-k or 'k	foot-kip
ft.-lb. or ft-# or '#	foot-pound
in. or "	inch
in^2 or sq. in.	square inch
in^3 or cu. in.	cubic inch
in.-kip. or in.-k or "k	inch-kip
in.-lb. or in-# or "#	inch-pound
kip or k	kip (1 kip = 1 kilo pound or 1,000 pounds)
ksi or k/in^2	kips per square inch
lb. or #	pound
lb./cu. ft. or $\#/ft^3$ or pcf	pounds per cubic foot
plf or #/' or #/ft.	pounds per lineal foot
psf or $\#/ft^2$	pounds per square foot
psi or $\#/in^2$	pounds per square inch
Δ (delta)	1. total strain (deformation)
	2. thermal expansion or contraction
	3. deflection
θ (theta)	a common designation for an angle
π (pi)	the ratio of the circumference of a circle to its diameter, equal to 3.14159
Σ (sigma)	summation of
φ (phi)	strength reduction factor in reinforced concrete design
#	pounds

QUESTIONS

1. The National Electrical Code (NEC) contains regulations concerning the number and placement of receptacles in residential dwelling units. Which of the following is NOT one of these regulations?

   A. Hallways that are less than six feet long do not require receptacles.

   B. In any continuous length of wall, receptacles cannot be further apart than 12 feet.

   C. A required kitchen receptacle must not be higher than 18 inches above a countertop.

   D. Except in bathrooms, any wall at least two feet long must have a receptacle.

2. Emergency exiting of handicapped people from the upper floors of a multi-story building requires special consideration. For example, an appropriate method would be the use of

   I. elevators connected to heat responsive call buttons.

   II. safe refuge areas within rated stairwells.

   III. ramps to the ground floor.

   A. I only

   B. II only

   C. III only

   D. II or III

3. Building codes require that certain critical building elements have a fire-resistive rating. For example, an exit stairwell in a two-story office building of Type IV construction requires a minimum rating of

   A. one-half hour.

   B. one hour.

   C. two hours.

   D. three hours.

4. For the design of a civic auditorium with a total of 722 seats, the minimum number of water closets required for the men's toilet room is _____. Use the table below.

Minimum Plumbing Facilities

Type of Building or Occupancy	Water Closets (Fixtures per Person)		Urinals (Fixtures per Male)	Lavatories (Fixtures per Person)	
	Male	Female		Male	Female
Assembly places (theatres, auditoriums, convention halls, etc.)— for permanent employee use	1:1-15 2:16-35 3:36-55 Over 55, add 1 fixture for each additional 40 persons	1:1-15 2:16-35 3:36-55	1 per 50	1 per 40	1 per 40
Assembly places (theaters, auditoriums, convention halls, etc.)—for public use	1:1-100 2:101-200 3:201-400	3:1-100 6:101-200 8:201-400	1:1-100 2:101-200 3:201-400 4:401-600	1:1-200 2:201-400 3:401-750	1:1-200 2:201-400 3:401-750

5. What is the minimum required clear distance from the face of an electrical panel to the nearest obstruction?

   A. 24 inches

   B. 36 inches

   C. 48 inches

   D. 72 inches

6. Select the correct statement about mass walls from those that follow.

   I. Mass walls are examples of active solar design.

   II. Mass walls operate on a cycle of storing and releasing heat.

   III. Mass walls utilize direct solar gain to heat buildings.

   IV. Two types of mass walls are trombe and water walls.

   A. I and II

   B. I and III

   C. III and IV

   D. II, III, and IV

1

7. An early example of passive solar heating is featured in a house designed by Frank Lloyd Wright near Madison, Wisconsin. Built for the Herbert Jacobs family in the mid 1940s, the project is known as the Solar Hemicycle house. Although displaying unusual energy awareness for its time, the design does NOT take advantage of

    A. high ceilings to promote convection for summer cooling.

    B. locating the north face of the building underground for insulation.

    C. utilizing solar radiant heat in floors and walls of the house.

    D. elongating the plan in an east-west direction to maximize solar heat gain.

8. You are the architect for a 100,000-square-foot office building, and the owner has asked you to incorporate energy-conserving techniques into your design. For purposes of analysis, you have separated the building's energy-consuming components into six categories as follows.

    I. Heating

    II. Cooling

    III. Domestic hot water

    IV. Vertical transportation

    V. Lighting

    VI. HVAC fans

    Rank these categories according to their average energy consumption, from highest to lowest.

    A. I, II, V, VI, III, IV

    B. II, I, VI, V, IV, III

    C. V, I, II, VI, IV, III

    D. V, VI, II, I, III, IV

9. Which of the following statements about energy conservation is correct?

    I. Because the north and west sides of a building are often subject to cold winds, entrances on these sides should be avoided if possible.

    II. A square building will usually experience less heat gain or loss than a rectangular building of equal area.

    III. Heat transmission through glass can be reduced to a level comparable to that of a solid wall by using double- or triple-glazing.

    IV. Reducing the lighting level in a building also reduces the amount of heating and cooling required for the building.

    A. All of the above   C. I and II

    B. II and III   D. I and III

10. The best method to reduce solar heat gain through windows is with the use of

    A. Venetian blinds.

    B. exterior shutters.

    C. draperies.

    D. double-glazing.

11. Some passive solar systems employ a conventional-type greenhouse that is attached to a structure. Which of the following statements about this system is incorrect?

    A. This system also employs a thermal storage wall.

    B. This system is virtually the same as a thermal storage wall system.

    C. This system is easily added to the south wall of an existing building.

    D. This system allows one to grow fresh vegetables throughout the year.

12. A Trombe wall is based on which of the following principles?

    I. The air between the glass layer and the mass wall only rises into the building when it has been heated.

    II. The mass wall absorbs a great deal of radiation without a rapid increase in temperature, and releases it again without a rapid drop in temperature.

    III. The mass wall causes a time delay when transferring the heat into the building, allowing it to arrive later, at night.

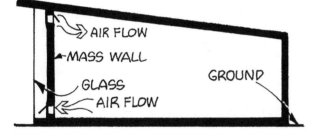

SECTION THROUGH TROMBE WALL

    A. I, II, and III
    B. I and II
    C. II and III
    D. I and III

13. The R-value of a wall assembly is related to which of the following?

    I. Conduction through the wall
    II. The temperature gradient between the interior and exterior
    III. The resistance of the wall's component parts

    A. I
    B. II
    C. I and III
    D. I, II, and III

14. When is the solar load at its lowest in North America?

    A. March 21
    B. June 21
    C. September 21
    D. December 21

15. A material would make a good solar collection panel if it has

    A. low emissivity in one wavelength and high absorptivity in another.
    B. high emissivity in one wavelength and low absorptivity in another.
    C. high emissivity in one wavelength and low emissivity in another.
    D. high absorptivity in one wavelength and low absorptivity in another.

16. A solar device consisting of either a parabolic trough or dish or an arrangement of lenses is a

    A. flat plate collector.
    B. focusing collector.
    C. fresnel lens.
    D. roof pond.

17. Indoor air quality (IAQ) may be adversely affected by which of the following? Check all that apply.

    A. Solar orientation
    B. Ventilation rate
    C. Smoking
    D. Building materials
    E. Prevailing winds
    F. Exterior temperature

18. Using the solar plot for 52°N Latitude shown below, what is the approximate altitude and azimuth at 10:00 AM on September 21 is _____.

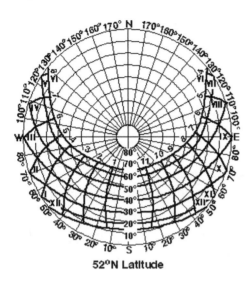

52°N Latitude

19. Air expands when it is heated, which reduces its density and makes it lighter. What is the only material that expands when it gets colder?

   A.   Steel

   B.   Wood

   C.   Concrete

   D.   Water

20. The presence of which of the following is considered LEAST harmful in a potable water supply?

   A.   Carcinogens

   B.   High acidity

   C.   Fluorine

   D.   Magnesium

21. The city of Columbus, Ohio, is located at 40 degrees north latitude. Using the solar plot provided, what is the sun's altitude and azimuth at 8 AM on April 1?

   A.   The altitude is 20 degrees and the azimuth is 70 degrees.

   B.   The altitude is 30 degrees and the azimuth is 80 degrees.

   C.   The altitude is 40 degrees and the azimuth is 40 degrees.

   D.   The altitude is 80 degrees and the azimuth is 30 degrees.

22. The owners of a company have asked the design team to consider sustainability in the design of their new building. Which of the following site characteristics will have the greatest impact on the building's mechanical systems?

   A.   Solar orientation

   B.   Prevailing wind direction

   C.   Views

   D.   Location of on-site water courses

23. Traps are provided in plumbing fixture drain lines in order to

   A.   intercept solid objects that might impede water flow.

   B.   maintain an unobstructed vent.

   C.   prevent sewer gases from entering a building.

   D.   reduce the noise of water flow through the system.

24. Sanitary waste differs from water supply in that it

   A. is usually moved under pressure, whereas water supply is not.

   B. is usually in larger pipes than water supply.

   C. can be mixed with storm drainage and sent to a sewage treatment plant.

   D. cannot be sent to cesspools or leach fields.

25. Which of the following represents a highly alkaline pH reading?

   A. 2

   B. 7

   C. 12

   D. 17

26. The primary purpose of a plumbing fixture vent is to

   A. permit escape of water vapor from the piping system.

   B. prevent leakage of sewer gas into occupied spaces.

   C. prevent siphoning of the trap seal.

   D. allow access of a plumber's snake to clear obstructions.

27. Which of the following is NOT a backflow preventer?

   A. Double check valve

   B. Gate valve

   C. Vacuum breaker

   D. Air gap fitting

28. Which among the following piping materials would satisfactorily serve a domestic water system? Check all that apply.

   A. Copper

   B. Lead

   C. Cement-lined cast iron

   D. Plastic

   E. Galvanized steel

   F. Aluminum

29. Which of the following devices is used to prevent sewer gasses from backing up into the building?

   A. Arrestor

   B. Valve

   C. Trap

   D. Stack

30. A device that is designed to prevent grease or oil from entering the sanitary system is called a

   A. trap.

   B. interceptor.

   C. valve.

   D. cleanout.

31. To what height will 50 psi of pressure lift a 3-inch-diameter column of water?

   A. 4 feet, 2 inches

   B. 50 feet

   C. 100 feet

   D. 115 feet

32. If the public water service provides water at 100 psi, and there is a friction loss of 15 psi between the street and the building, what is the highest floor on which a faucet may be placed if the faucet requires 15 psi? Assume that each floor is 12 feet high.

   A. 8 stories

   B. 9 stories

   C. 13 stories

   D. 14 stories

33. The comfort zone generally ranges from about 73°F to 77°F and between 20 percent and 60 percent relative humidity (RH). If intake air in a system is 80°F and 10 percent RH, how should this air be treated so it will conform to comfort zone standards?

   I. Remove latent heat from the air

   II. Remove sensible heat from the air

   III. Add moisture to the air

   A. I only

   B. II only

   C. III only

   D. I and III

34. Air filtration, which comprises an integral part of all HVAC systems, has as its principal purpose the elimination of

   A. offensive odors.

   B. unpleasant mechanical noises.

   C. interior pollutants.

   D. atmospheric particles.

35. Which of the following heat transfer processes are affected by relative humidity?

   A. Convection

   B. Radiation

   C. Latent heat

   D. Conduction

36. The return duct of a centralized air-conditioning system

   A. returns the air from the air-conditioned rooms back to the central supply fan.

   B. aids the supply fan in providing air to the distant corners of the building.

   C. exhausts air from the building.

   D. provides outside air to the building.

37. Heat transfers across a vacuum by means of

   A. radiation.

   B. conduction.

   C. convection.

   D. None of the above

38. Relative humidity is a comfort factor because of which of the following heat transfer processes?

   A. Radiation

   B. Conduction

   C. Convection

   D. Latent heat

39. The heating and cooling capacities of a plant are measured in

   I. Btuh.

   II. tons.

   III. U-value.

   A. I, II, and III

   B. I and II

   C. II and III

   D. I and III

40. When performing cooling load calculations, heat generated by which of the following must be taken into account? Check all that apply.

    A. Friction
    B. People
    C. Lighting
    D. Fixed equipment
    E. Portable equipment
    F. Prevailing winds

41. The amount by which the average outdoor temperature at a given location is below 65°F for one day is called a(n)

    A. degree day.
    B. design day.
    C. chill factor.
    D. effective temperature.

42. What is the definition of dew point?

    A. The temperature at which the moisture contained in the air begins to evaporate
    B. The temperature at which the humidity contained in the air begins to lower
    C. The temperature at which the moisture contained in the air begins to condense
    D. The temperature at which the humidity contained in the air begins to rise

43. Evaporative cooling is most appropriate in a climate that is

    A. mild and dry.
    B. mild and humid.
    C. warm and dry.
    D. warm and humid.

44. Which of the all-water HVAC hydronic systems shown below is the most versatile and energy efficient?

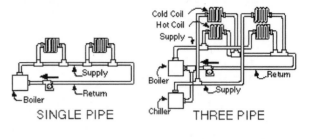

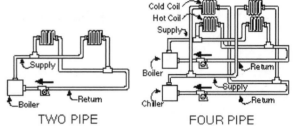

    A. Single pipe
    B. Two pipe
    C. Three pipe
    D. Four pipe

45. Evaporative coolers are inexpensive, relatively effective, and popular. However, they

    A. do not actually change the heat content of the indoor air.
    B. require a relatively high amount of energy to operate.
    C. produce a cooler feeling by reducing the humidity in the air.
    D. are not particularly effective in hot, arid climates.

46. Of the following statements regarding forced-air HVAC systems, which is NOT true?

    A. Forced-air systems are so named for the fan that forces air through supply ducts.

    B. Forced-air systems pressurize buildings to eliminate infiltration.

    C. Supply ducts are insulated on the inside for sound and outside for temperature.

    D. In harsh climates, outside air intake should be limited to reduce costs.

47. Which of the following BEST describes a two-pipe system?

    A. Hot water flows in one pipe and chilled water flows in the other pipe.

    B. The north side of a building can be heated and the south side can be cooled simultaneously.

    C. It requires one pump only.

    D. It requires a hot water and chilled water pump.

48. The refrigeration cycle uses all of the following devices EXCEPT a(n)

    A. compressor.

    B. evaporator coil.

    C. condenser coil.

    D. economizer.

49. Which of the following systems can provide heating and cooling to different zones simultaneously?

    A. Variable air volume (VAV) with electric reheat

    B. Two-pipe system

    C. Single duct constant volume

    D. None of the above

50. Which type of duct results in the least amount of friction loss?

    A. Square duct

    B. Rectangular duct

    C. Oval duct

    D. Round duct

51. A device through which the air from a duct passes before entering a room is a

    A. diffuser.

    B. grille.

    C. turning vane.

    D. damper.

52. Using the table below, the maximum heat gain from 12 people working in a secretarial pool is _____.

Btuh for Various Activities

Degree of Activity	Typical Application	Total Heat Adults, Male Btu/h	Sensible Heat Btu/h	Latent Heat Btu/h
Seated at rest	Theater, movie	400	210	140
Seated, very light work, writing	Offices, hotels, apts	480	230	190
Seated, eating	Restaurant	520	255	325
Seated, light work, typing	Offices, hotels, apts	640	255	255
Standing, light work or walking slowly	Retail store, bank	800	315	325
Light bench work	Factory	880	345	435
Walking, 3 mph, light machine work	Factory	1040	345	695

53. If a wall has a total thermal resistance R-25.4, the U-value of the wall is _____. Give your answer with four decimal places.

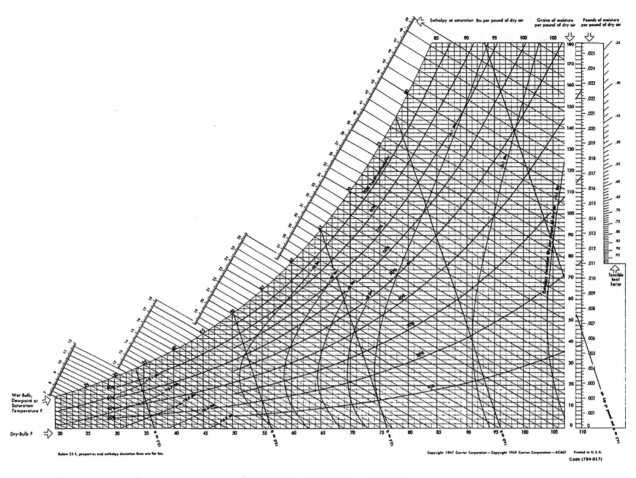

PSYCHROMETRIC CHART

(A larger version of the psychrometric chart can be found on page 67 of the Study Guide.)

54. Given the psychrometric chart above, if the dry bulb temperature is 70°F and the relative humidity is 60 percent, the wet bulb temperature is _____.

55. A large family room requires two light switches to control the same light fixture. What is the number and type of switches that should be provided?

A. 2 two-way switches

B. 2 three-way switches

C. 1 one-way switch and 1 two-way switch

D. 2 four-way switches

56. In an overhead power district, the power company may provide service

I. underground.

II. overhead.

III. underground if the owner provides the conduit between the building and the power pole.

IV. underground if the conduit is encased in concrete.

A. II only

B. I, II, III, and IV

C. II and III

D. III and IV

57. The flow of electricity is affected by all of the following EXCEPT

    A. potential.

    B. current.

    C. power.

    D. resistance.

58. Devices that change the voltage of an AC circuit to a higher or lower value are called

    A. solenoids.

    B. motors.

    C. alternators.

    D. transformers.

59. Three-phase, four-wire electrical systems in modern buildings serve

    A. lighting.

    B. power.

    C. lighting and power.

    D. motors.

60. Which of the following are characteristics of a VAV system? Check all that apply.

    A. Conserves fan energy during light loads

    B. Modulates the supply air temperature very closely

    C. Requires no return air duct

    D. Is easily adaptable to changing zones or adding zones in the future

    E. Allows different areas to be heated and cooled simultaneously

    F. Allows control of temperature in each zone

61. A type of power delivered with three separate circuits that have frequencies 120 degrees out of phase with each other is

    A. three-phase service.

    B. single-phase service.

    C. alternating current.

    D. direct current.

62. Which type of conduit may NOT be embedded in concrete?

    A. Rigid conduit

    B. Armored cable

    C. Electrical metallic tubing

    D. Flexible metal conduit

63. The resistance of a hair dryer that draws 11 amperes at 120 volts is _____.

64. If the voltage between the neutral and the peak of a three-phase current is 120 volts, the voltage between two phases is _____.

65. The recommended luminance level necessary for routine office work, such as reading and writing, is

    A. 30 footcandles.

    B. 50 footcandles.

    C. 70 footcandles.

    D. 150 footcandles.

66. Illumination is best defined as

    A. the amount of light generated by a source.

    B. the amount of light falling on one square foot of a surface.

    C. the amount of light reflected from one square foot of a surface.

    D. the amount of light flowing through a hypothetical one-foot square located one foot from a one-candlepower source.

67. The CRI of a fluorescent light source tells us whether the

    A. source is warm or cool in color rendition.

    B. source is energy efficient.

    C. source matches the color of an incandescent source at the same temperature.

    D. source has a long lamp life.

68. The percentage of solar heat transmitted by a given pane of glass compared to that transmitted by clear glass is called

    A. shading coefficient.

    B. clear coefficient.

    C. insulation.

    D. insolation.

69. Which portion of the eye focuses light on the retina?

    A. Cones

    B. Lens

    C. Iris

    D. None of the above

70. Which of the following lighting systems is most appropriate for a computer lab space?

    A. Indirect

    B. Semi-indirect

    C. Semi-direct

    D. Direct

71. Light reflectors and refractors are designed to

    A. provide a specific distribution of light.

    B. reduce glare.

    C. reduce veiling reflections.

    D. increase visibility.

72. Which type of lighting fixture provides the most diffuse light?

    A. Direct

    B. Indirect

    C. Semi-direct

    D. Semi-indirect

73. Which kind of lamp contains a filament that is heated by passing an electric current through it?

    A. Fluorescent

    B. Incandescent

    C. High intensity discharge

    D. None of the above

74. A material that both transmits and diffuses light is called

    A. transparent.

    B. translucent.

    C. reflective.

    D. opaque.

75. A 100' × 50' meeting room has a coefficient of utilization of 0.65, and a maintenance factor of 0.8. Using a three-lamp fluorescent light fixture with 2,800 lumens/lamp, _____ fixtures are needed to provide a light level of 50 footcandles.

76. If a lamp of 1,200 candlepower intensity results in an illumination of 12 footcandles at 10 feet, what is the illumination at 20 feet?

    A. 3 fc

    B. 6 fc

    C. 12 fc

    D. 24 fc

77. Given the photometric chart and lighting condition illustrated below, what is the illuminance on Surface A, directly beneath the light?

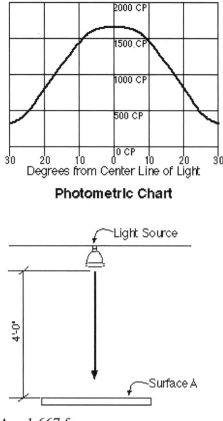

Photometric Chart

A. 1,667 fc

B. 417 fc

C. 104 fc

D. 32 fc

78. Among the following statements concerning acoustics, which is incorrect?

A. Sound waves are perfect sine waves.

B. Sound intensity is related to the distance from a source.

C. A 34-decibel sound has four times the intensity of a 28-decibel sound.

D. Humans are most sensitive to sounds in the middle frequencies.

79. Through a combination of surface treatments and transmission control, the sound intensity in an office has been reduced from 55 dB to 47 dB. This modification is considered to be

A. a substantial reduction in noise, resulting in a comfortable office environment.

B. an unnecessary change, since the office did not require modification to begin with.

C. a slight reduction in noise, leaving the office with an unacceptably high noise level.

D. a significant reduction in noise, but the noise level is still like a factory.

80. Several factors should be considered in order to achieve a good acoustic environment within a space. Which of the following is the LEAST important of these factors?

A. The texture of the materials in the space

B. The volume of the space

C. The use to which the space is put

D. The type of noise to which the space is subjected

81. Reflected sound paths that converge into certain areas of rooms is a condition known as

A. echoing.

B. focusing.

C. flutter.

D. diffusion.

82. A loud office has a noise level intensity of 70 decibels. In order to reduce the noise by 50 percent, as perceived by the average ear, the noise level would have to be reduced by

    A. 8 decibels.

    B. 17 decibels.

    C. 35 decibels.

    D. 70 decibels.

83. With regard to effective acoustical design, select the incorrect statement from among those that follow.

    A. Spaces that are designed as pure geometrical shapes should be avoided.

    B. Concave wall surfaces within spaces are preferable to convex wall surfaces.

    C. Reverberation is rarely a problem in a very small space.

    D. In very large spaces, reverberation time can be as long as a half minute.

84. In designing a concert hall the acoustical engineer would, most likely, recommend a reverberation time of approximately

    A. zero.

    B. two seconds.

    C. five seconds.

    D. ten seconds.

85. Which of the following is LEAST likely to be controlled by a building automation system?

    A. HVAC system

    B. Drinking fountains

    C. Fire detection and alarm system

    D. Elevators

86. Which of the following is NOT a component of a data cabling network?

    A. Hub

    B. Switch

    C. Panelboard

    D. Patch panel

87. In selecting elevators for a multi-story office building, which of the following factors should be considered in determining the capacity or number required? Check all that apply.

    A. Height of the building

    B. Location of dry standpipes

    C. Weight of building equipment

    D. Emergency evacuation standards

    E. Number of occupants at the highest floor

    F. Building functions and schedule

88. Select the correct statement from among the following.

    A. Maximum elevator traffic in a building is generally computed at several different times during the day.

    B. Elevator traffic generally reaches its maximum peak during lunch time.

    C. Elevator capacity is computed on the basis of car size.

    D. Elevator capacity is computed on the basis of travel speed.

89. Of the following vertical transportation systems, which one is most suitable for the occupants in a highrise office building?

    A. Hydraulic passenger elevator

    B. Electric passenger elevator

    C. Freight elevator

    D. Escalator

90. A ram-driven vertical transportation system that is best suited for lowrise buildings and has a travel speed of between 25 and 150 feet per minute (fpm) is a(n)

   A. electric elevator.

   B. hydraulic elevator.

   C. escalator.

   D. None of the above

91. The most common type of sprinkler system used for fire suppression is

   A. preaction.

   B. deluge.

   C. wet-pipe.

   D. dry-pipe.

92. Halon has notable flame-extinguishing capabilities, as well as which of the following characteristics?

   I. Its use is appropriate for all classes of fires.

   II. Embers can reignite when the gas dissipates.

   III. It does not harm building contents.

   IV. Its use requires audible and visible warnings for people to leave the area.

   A. I only

   B. III only

   C. II and III

   D. I, II, and IV

93. A fire that involves flammable gases and liquids, such as gasoline or propane, is described as what class of fire?

   A. Class A

   B. Class B

   C. Class C

   D. Class D

94. Which of the following is NOT used as a fire extinguishing media?

   A. Water

   B. Halon

   C. Carbon dioxide

   D. Carbon monoxide

95. An effective means of preventing the spread of smoke is to use mechanically regulated smoke control. In order for this technique to operate, which of the following must occur in the event of fire?

   A. Exhaust dampers in the fire area must be fully closed.

   B. Supply dampers in the fire area must be fully closed.

   C. Supply fans serving the fire area increase their speed.

   D. Exhaust fans serving the fire area decrease their speed.

96. A wall has a U-value of 0.20. In order to reduce heat transmission through the wall, 1½ inches of insulation having a K-value of 0.30 is added. The R-value of the wall after adding the insulation is _____.

97. A new 50,000 square foot office building has a total construction cost of $120.00 per square foot. What is a reasonable cost estimate for the building's electrical and mechanical systems?

   A. $500,000

   B. $1,000,000

   C. $1,800,000

   D. $3,000,000

98. If the ridgeline of a gable-roofed house is 24 feet above grade, and the fireplace chimney is 8 feet from the ridgeline, then what is the required height above grade of the chimney?

99. If a central heating furnace not listed for alcove or closet installation were 3 feet wide × 6 feet long and 5 feet high and installed in a room with an 8-foot ceiling, then what would the area of the room need to be according to UBC and Uniform Plumbing code (which require room volume to be 12 times the volume of the furnace)?

100. Sustainable design has made the economic decision process more holistic and is now concerned with "life cycle" cost of the design. Which of the following factors are related to "life cycle" costs the architect and owner can evaluate? Check the four that apply.

   A. The first cost to produce or manufacture a building product or assembly

   B. The energy used to transport the product to the building site

   C. Operating and maintenance costs

   D. Periodic replacement cost

   E. The residual value of the design element

   F. The cost to recycle the outdated design element

101. The goal of LEED (Leadership in Energy & Environmental Design) and similar environmental design standards, is to introduce new sustainable approaches and technologies to the construction industry. Which of the following are categories within the LEED rating system? Check the four that apply.

   A. Indoor air quality

   B. Water efficiency

   C. Energy and Atmosphere

   D. Psychological Influences of environment

   E. Materials and Resources

   F. Indigenous Solar Design Styles

102. Which of the following describe Passive Solar Design Strategies? Check the four that apply.

   A. Thermal Storage Walls

   B. Overhangs or Shading devices

   C. Dark-Colored Roof Systems

   D. Low-E Glass

   E. Roof Decks

   F. Grass or vegetated roof areas

103. Which of the following are part of a holistic approach to lighting sustainably designed spaces? Check the four that apply.

   A. Light Shelves

   B. Fixtures producing fewer lumens per watt

   C. LED lighting for exit signs

   D. Higher Efficiency Light Fixtures

   E. Fixtures with dimming and multiple switching capability

   F. Bubble Skylights for natural light

104. A 9-story building has a floor-to-floor height of 11 feet. A pressure of 15 psi is required to flush a toilet. What is the required water pressure at the base of the building?

105. Which of the following materials are used in modern plumbing installations? Check the three that apply.

    A. Galvanized steel

    B. Black iron

    C. Copper tubing

    D. PVC plastic pipe

    E. ABS zinc pipe

106. Which of the following types of valves are used in plumbing systems? Check the four that apply.

    A. Gate valve

    B. Access valve

    C. Globe valve

    D. Check valve

    E. Angle valve

    F. Water hammer valve

107. Which of the following statements are correct concerning the effects of acidic water? Check the three that apply.

    A. Acidic water causes deposition, so pipes should be oversized.

    B. PVC pipe is not appropriate for supply piping in exposed locations above ground.

    C. Copper and PVC are resistant to corrosion and therefore appropriate where water is acidic.

    D. Plastic pipe does not allow the electrolysis that deposits mineral ions.

    E. Acidic water can be controlled by using the zeolite or ion exchange process.

108. Which of the following statements accurately describe the Convection Process? Check the three that apply.

    A. Convection occurs only in a fluid medium, such as air or liquid.

    B. Water is the only material that expands when it gets colder.

    C. Convection occurs in rooms only when the temperature shifts suddenly.

    D. Convection is the only means of heat transfer that is strictly directional.

    E. Convection never transfers heat downwards or horizontally.

    F. Convection does not occur within heavily insulated wall cavities.

109. CLTD approximates the effects of which of the following? Check the four that apply.

    A. Radiation

    B. Conduction

    C. Convection

    D. Wall Mass

    E. Latent Heat

    F. Orientation and Color

110. Which of the following statements correctly describe attributes of Relative Humidity? Check the two that apply.

    A. A constant amount of water in the air represents a constant relative humidity.

    B. Relative humidity is defined as the percentage of complete saturation (how much water is in the air at a given temperature compared to how much the air could hold at that temperature).

    C. Air can hold much more water when it is warm than when it is cold.

    D. We always put a vapor barrier on the cool side of the insulation in a wall.

    E. In the United States, for people doing sedentary work who are lightly clothed, the Comfort Zone ranges from about 45% to 88% RH.

    F. Moving air shifts the comfort zone to slightly lower temperatures.

111. Which of the following are elements of Active Solar Systems? Check the four that apply.

    A. A flat plate collector

    B. A trombe collector

    C. A bent fresnal lens

    D. Photovoltaic cells

    E. Amorphous silicon cells

    F. A nighttime flushing system

112. The time of day affects which of the following factors? Check the three that apply.

    A. The declination angle

    B. The altitude angle

    C. The azimuth angle

    D. The intensity of the sun

    E. The speed of transit

113. Which of the following are correct descriptions of parts of the Refrigeration Cycle? Check the three that apply.

    A. The refrigeration cycle uses a special fluid, Freon, circulated in an open loop.

    B. The pressure in the loop causes changes in the temperature, evaporation but not in the condensation.

    C. Evaporation goes on at a very low temperature and absorbs heat from its surroundings.

    D. The evaporative chiller is often called a cooling tower.

    E. In seasons when it is cool enough outside, the outside air may be used directly and the refrigeration cycle shut off.

    F. Cool water from exterior ponds is never used instead of chilled refrigerant water due to the potential presence of bacteria.

114. Which of the following describe the basic categories in Mechanical Equipment Distribution Systems? Check the three that apply.

    A. Electrical Systems

    B. Hydronic Systems

    C. Radiant Systems

    D. Forced Air Systems

    E. Two-, Three-, and Four-pipe Systems

115. Which of the following statements accurately describe Forced Air Systems? Check the three that apply.

    A. Forced air systems distribute heated or cooled air around the building using supply ducts.

    B. Fresh air intakes should be located adjacent to the cooling tower but away from other exhausts.

    C. To eliminate infiltration in a building, we positively pressurize the building by running the supply fan at a rate lower than the sum of the return air fan rate and the leakage rate of the building.

    D. Fans must be isolated from floors and ducts in order to reduce vibrational noise throughout the building.

    E. The double duct system is also called a Fan Coil system because it can heat and cool simultaneously.

    F. The most common efficient system is the variable air volume VAV system.

116. Cooling loads are often expressed in tonnage. How many Btuh would melt two tons of ice over a 24-hour period?

117. The friction of the air traveling through the ducts must be considered in sizing ducts. If the friction loss becomes excessive, then larger duct sizes can be chosen or special fans specified. The friction loss is expressed in inches of water per 100 feet, also known as the static head. How many inches of static head are required to support a 12-inch column of water?

118. Direct current (DC) means current that flows only in one direction, with constant voltage. This is typical for low voltage applications such as batteries. What is the Direct Current produced by a 12 volt battery connected to a 4 ohm resistor?

119. Which of the following statements accurately describe Transformers (the devices that change the voltage of an AC circuit to a higher or lower value)? Check the three that apply.

    A. A transformer consists of an iron core on which two separate coils of wire are wound.

    B. While a transformer changes the voltage in a circuit, it has practically no effect on the total power in the circuit.

    C. Transformers are called step down transformers when they increase the voltage in a building.

    D. Transformers do not waste energy.

    E. Transformers do not need to be ventilated since they are insulated by a fluid that insulates the electricity and cools the transformer.

    F. Transformers must either be placed outside the building, or within the building inside a fireproof vault.

120. Which of the following types of motors are in general use? Choose the four that apply.

    A. DC Motors

    B. Thermal Relay Motor

    C. Single-Phase AC Motors

    D. Three-Phase Induction Motors

    E. Universal Motors

    F. Wye Motor

121. Early in a project it might be necessary for the architect to estimate the overall electrical load. This can be done by estimating the wattage per square foot, based on general experience for various building functions. Which of the following should be included in this estimate? Check the three that apply.

    A. Lighting Load (estimate 2-5 watts/sf)

    B. Lighting Load (estimate 5-10 watts/sf)

    C. Convenience Outlet Load (estimate 1-3 watts/sf)

    D. Convenience Outlet Load (estimate 2-5 watts/sf)

    E. HVAC Load (estimate 2-4 watts/sf)

    F. HVAC Load (estimate 4-7 watts/sf)

122. How many amps are now required for the minimum electrical service in a residence?

123. Given three parallel paths, two paths with a resistance of 4 ohms and one with a resistance of 2 ohms, what is the total net resistance?

124. If the voltage between the neutral and the peak of a three-phase current is 120 volts, what is the voltage between two phases?

125. If we were to place a candle one foot from a blackboard, how many lumens would arrive on one square foot of blackboard surface?

126. If a lamp has an intensity of 1,200 fc (footcandles), then what is the illumination (E) on a perpendicular surface 8 feet away?

127. If a lamp shines on a wall 10 feet away and produces an illumination of 24 fc, then how many fc will illuminate a wall located 20 feet away?

128. Which of the following are TRUE about fluorescent lighting? Check all that apply.

    A. Fluorescent lighting is more efficient than incandescent lighting.

    B. Fluorescent lighting can have different CRI ratings, depending on the specific phosphors used.

    C. Warm White fluorescent lamps produce the most lumens per watt.

    D. Fluorescent lighting does not run on 12 volt DC current.

    E. The lifetime of a fluorescent tube is determined by the number of hours it is lit.

    F. Mercury vapor fluorescent fixtures typically have a lifetime in the 24,000 hour range.

129. The Daylight Factor Method calculates the amount of light at a particular interior location as a percentage of the light which is available on an exterior horizontal surface. For example, a DF (daylight factor) of 4 in a workstation 25 feet from the window means that 4% of the light available outside would arrive on the counter in the workstation, which may be fine given the high outside light level. If there were 1,800 fc on the ground outside, then what would be the illumination on the workstation counter in this example?

130. Acoustically, although doubling the distance from the source to the receiver cuts the intensity to one quarter (remember the inverse square law), this results in a change of only 6 dB in intensity level. If an office worker sits 15 feet away from a busy street and experiences an IL of 80 dB, then what is the decibel level for her co-worker who sits 45 feet further inside the building?

131. Doubling the number of sources at a given intensity would result in a gain of how many decibels?

132. What is the total absorptivity (in sabins) of an empty classroom at 2,000 Hz?

    A. The room is 12 feet × 15 feet in plan with a 10-foot-high ceiling.

    B. The floor is carpet on concrete (with a Sound Absorption Coefficient of .60)

    C. The four walls are one-half inch gypsum board on 2 × 4 studs (Coefficient of .07)

    D. The ceiling is smooth finish plaster on lath (Coefficient of .04)

133. What is the reverberation time (the amount of time that elapses before there is complete silence after a 60 dB sound has stopped) for the classroom in the previous question? (Use the equation $T_R = .049 \, V/A$)

134. How long must a handicapped ramp be in order to connect two levels whose difference of elevation is two feet?

135. Which of the following statements correctly describe Traction Elevators? Check the four that apply.

    A. Oil serves as the pressure fluid, the supply of which is controlled by high-speed pumps.

    B. They are generally used in commercial and institutional buildings greater than 50 feet in height.

    C. On one end of the cables is the elevator car, and on the other end are counterweights.

    D. The motor and drum assembly that moves the elevator car is called a traction machine.

    E. Gearless machines are used for high-speed installations.

    F. Elevator platforms sit over a plunger, or ram, which operates in a cylinder.

136. What is the rated elevator speed for an electric elevator serving a 360-foot-high building?

137. Escalators are used to move large numbers of people from floor to floor quickly, efficiently, safely (safer than stairs), and at relatively low cost. The normal angle of incline is approximately how many degrees?

138. If the total Occupant Load to be served by a corridor in a building is 120 occupants, then what is the minimum exit width required in inches?

1. **A.** All of the statements are actual regulations, with the exception of correct choice A. All dwelling unit spaces require receptacles, including hallways. In fact, a receptacle is required in any wall that is two feet or greater in length, except in bathrooms (choice D).

2. **B.** An elevator, even with heat responsive call buttons (I), should never be used as an emergency exit because the shaft conducts smoke and flames, like a chimney. Most elevators are programmed to return to the lobby in the event of a fire. Providing ramps to the ground (III) works well for low-rise buildings, but for multi-story buildings, ramps to the ground are simply impractical. The most reasonable solution for handicapped persons is to provide safety waiting, or refuge, areas within stairwells (II and correct choice B). Fire personnel are aware of these areas and will assist those persons needing to be rescued. Refuge areas must be located out of the direct exit pathway so as not to reduce the required exit width of the stairway.

3. **B.** Buildings of Type III and Type V construction that are under five stories in height are required to have exit stairs with a one-hour fire-resistive rating (answer B). The purpose of all ratings is to assure that occupants will have sufficient time to exit the building in the event of a fire. For example, the one-hour rating assures that occupants will have an hour to exit by stairwell. Every component of the stairway enclosure must be rated one hour: the walls, doors, jambs, and all other openings. Buildings that are more than five stories in height, or of Type I or II construction, require a minimum fire-resistive rating of two hours for all exit stair enclosures.

4. **Three.** The answer is three water closets. The table is arranged so that the first number preceding the colon is the required number of fixtures, and the range of values after the colon represents the number of people that can be accommodated. The maximum number of people in this auditorium will be 722, of which half, or 361, are assumed to be male. Under the Water Closet heading for Males, 361 falls between 201 and 400, and therefore three fixtures are required. Also, note that the requirements for Urinals are the same, and under Lavatories for Males, 361 also falls between 201 and 400, so two lavatories are required.

5. **B.** According to the National Electric Code (NEC), a minimum of 36 inches of clear space must be maintained in front of an electric panel to facilitate safe access and servicing (B is correct).

6. **D.** A mass wall is a solar design device that uses the mass of a material to absorb direct solar radiation. Statement I is incorrect because a mass wall is an example of passive solar design, not active. Mass walls absorb solar radiation during the day and slowly release heat during the night (II). Spaces near a mass wall are heated by radiation of the stored solar energy (III). Two types of mass walls are water walls and trombe walls (IV). Water walls use tubes of water as the storage mass. The trombe wall is an effective passive device because it not only uses the mass of the wall for solar storage, but it may also use the space between the glass and the wall for a convective loop. By placing one-way vents at the top and bottom of the wall, rising heated air exits through the top vent and is distributed through the space. Cold air in the space is drawn through

the lower vent and is heated by solar radiation coming through the glass. The convection process repeats and is referred as thermosiphoning.

7. A.   In his Solar Hemicycle house, Frank Lloyd Wright created an arc of stone that shields a sunken circular garden against the prevailing winds. Most of the north face of the building is placed underground (choice B), using the thermal mass of the bermed earth for insulation. Large areas of glazing face south, with allows the winter sun's radiant heat to be absorbed by the floor and interior north wall (choice C). In addition, the elongated east-west floor plan (choice D) maximizes solar radiant heat gain. Only choice A is an incorrect statement, because the ceilings in this house are fairly low. Cooling in the summer is achieved by overhangs that block the sun and by large door openings along the south elevation that allow breezes to pass freely through the building.

8. C.   In a recent study by the AIA Research Corporation, it was determined that lighting (V) is typically the largest energy user in an office building, accounting for about 35 percent of total building energy consumption. The other energy consumers, in order, are heating (I) (26 percent), cooling (II) (17 percent), HVAC fans (VI) (11 percent), vertical transportation (IV) (8 percent), and domestic hot water (III) (4 percent). The ranking is shown correctly in choice C.

9. C.   Energy conservation in buildings involves a great many variables, including the building's orientation, site, materials, fenestration, mechanical and electrical systems, and so on. There is no single approach to energy conservation; rather, it is important to have an understanding of all the various factors that affect a building's use of energy. Although a site's microclimate must be considered, it is generally true that the north and west sides of a building are most subject to cold winds (I). If possible, therefore, entrances and glazed openings on these sides should be avoided. The heat gain or loss of a building is a function of its surface area. Because a square building has less surface area than a rectangular building of equal floor area, it experiences less heat gain or loss (II). Double-glazing has a U-value of about 0.60, about half that of single-glazing. Triple-glazing has a U-value of about 0.40. But the U-value of a solid wall is even lower—an insulated masonry or concrete wall has a U-value of around 0.10 to 0.20, which can be reduced to 0.04 or even less. Statement III is therefore untrue. A building's lighting system also produces heat. Reducing the lighting level, therefore, has two effects: in the summer, with less heat given off by the lighting, less cooling for the building is needed. During the heating season, however, with the lighting system generating less heat, more heat must come from the building's regular heating system. So, reducing the lighting level in a building increases the amount of heating required and decreases the amount of cooling required for the building. Statement IV is therefore incorrect. Answer C is correct.

10. B.   Because the object in reducing heat gain is to prevent solar energy from entering the building, it is always most effective to stop the radiation on the outside, before it reaches the glass. Therefore choice B is correct, as exterior shutters will shade the glass. Double-glazing reduces conduction gains and losses, but does very little to reduce solar radiation unless the glazing is reflective. Finally, Venetian blinds and draperies can do little more than trap the heat against the glass once it enters the building. At that point, however, solar heat gain has penetrated the space.

11. **B.**   An attached greenhouse solar system consists of a conventional greenhouse that is readily constructed on the south side of a structure (C), with a thermal mass storage wall separating the greenhouse from the rest of the building (A). It is essentially a combination of direct and indirect gain systems; that is, the greenhouse space is directly heated by sunlight, the back wall absorbs the heat, and a portion of this heat is transferred into the building. The system differs from a thermal storage wall system (incorrect statement and correct answer B), which is an indirect gain system. In such systems, sunlight strikes the thermal mass wall where it is absorbed by the mass, converted to thermal energy (heat), and then transferred to the rest of the building. Statement D expresses a unique advantage of the attached greenhouse solar system. The greenhouse area functions efficiently as a space in which plants can thrive throughout the year in almost any part of the country.

12. **A.**   All three statements are correct. The air between the glass layer and the mass wall only rises into the building when it is heated. At night, when it is cooled by losses to the outside, the air in the space sinks and pushes the lower duct flap shut, thus sealing the space from the building. The mass wall absorbs a great deal of radiation without a rapid increase in temperature, and releases it again without a rapid drop in temperature. This is beneficial in any storage medium, since we do not want large and rapid temperature fluctuation within the living

space of the building. The mass wall causes a time delay when transferring heat into the building, allowing it to arrive at night, when it is most needed. In fact, concrete and stone have roughly a one-hour time delay per inch of thickness.

13. **C.**   The R-value of a wall assembly is directly related to the sum of the R-value of the component parts (II is correct). In addition, some amount of heat will transfer through the wall by materials that are in direct contact with each other (I is correct). The temperature gradient between the interior and exterior will have an effect on the amount of heat transferred, and thus the temperature on the interior surface. However the gradient does not affect the wall's R-value, which is a constant regardless of temperature (C is correct).

14. **D.**   December 21 is the day of the winter solstice which is not only the shortest day of the year, but also the point during the year when the sun is at its lowest point in the sky. Consequently, the solar load on buildings is at its lowest on this day (B is correct).

15. **A.**   The emissivity of a surface is a property of the material, and is usually the same as the absorptivity at any given wavelength. The simplest example in the visible spectrum is color. Black surfaces have higher emissivities and absorptivities than white or shiny surfaces. Black surfaces heat up rapidly and cool off rapidly. Shiny surfaces heat up more slowly, but stay hot longer. The emissivity and absorptivity are often different between the infrared and visible spectrum. Selective surfaces are surfaces that have a high absorptivity in one wavelength (usually solar) and low emissivity in another (usually infrared). This means

that the material stores incoming solar radiation without releasing it as infrared (i.e., a good solar collector panel) (A is correct).

16. **B.**   A focusing collector consists of either a parabolic trough or a parabolic dish, or an arrangement of lenses, which focuses incoming light onto a tube or a point. It generates much higher energy densities and much higher temperatures than a flat plate collector (B is correct).

17. **B, C, and D.**   Indoor air quality (IAQ) may be adversely affected by building materials, ventilation, and smoking.

18. **30° altitude.**   A solar diagram is a map showing the sun's path across the sky. The concentric circles represent the altitude of the sun in 10° increments, with the other circle being the horizon and the inner cross 90°. The azimuth is represented by the radial lines, which are labeled in 10° increments from south to north. The lines that run from east to west and curve toward the south show the path of the sun for each month. The Roman numerals along the west and east represent the months. June (VI) and December (XII) are the solstice months and are at the outer ends of the plot. On the June plot, the numbers along the top represent the time of day. On the plot for 52°N Latitude, the longest day of the year beings about 4:00 AM and ends about 8:00 PM For this question, the day is September 21 and the time is 10:00 AM The September plot is the fourth from the bottom (month IV). The point where the September plot crosses the curved vertical line labeled 10:00 is where the altitude and azimuth are read. In this case, the altitude is 30°.

19. **D.**   The only material that expands when it gets colder is water (D is correct). This

fact necessitates careful construction detailing as water freezing inside joints will cause expansion and potential damage.

20. **C.**   Potable water, that is, water suitable for drinking, must be free of contaminants. Carcinogens (choice A), for example, are pollutants that contaminate underground water because hazardous chemicals have been improperly stored or discarded. Drinking such water increases one's risk of developing cancer. High acidity (choice B) rarely harms people, but in time it will corrode pipes and require their replacement. Fluorine (correct choice C) is often added to municipal water supplies to reduce the incidence of tooth decay. The benefits of fluoridation far outweigh the minor negative effects attributed to it. Magnesium (choice D) is a mineral that causes hard water, a condition that interferes with the sudsing action of soaps, and leaves a mineral residue in pipes and hot water heaters that may interfere with a water system's operation.

21. **B.**   Referring to the solar plot, find the curved line labeled with IV, which corresponds with the fourth month of the year (April) and follow it to the point where it crosses the 8:00 AM line labeled simply "8." Reading from this point, the concentric circles show the altitude is 30 degrees and the radial lines show the azimuth is 80 degrees (B is correct).

22. **A.**   The site's solar orientation will have the greatest impact on the building's mechanical systems. Solar radiation admitted through windows is among the highest sources of heat gain in buildings. Siting the building to limit this gain will have a significant impact on the overall size of the building's cooling plant (A is correct). The direction of the prevailing

winds, views, and location of water courses are all important considerations for the aesthetic quality of a project, but do not have a significant impact on mechanical systems (B, C, and D are incorrect).

23. **C.**   A trap is a water seal fitting, often U-shaped, which is located in the drain line after the fixture. As it is filled with water, it forms a trap that prevents sewer gases and odors from reversing their flow and entering a building (correct answer C). Special traps do exist for the purpose of catching solids (A), but these are exceptional cases, such as dentists' sinks, which are designed to recover gold and silver particles. Traps have no effect on vents (B); vents maintain atmospheric pressure in the drain so that water from the trap will not be siphoned. Finally, traps have little to do with creating or preventing plumbing noises (D).

24. **B.**   Sanitary waste is usually in larger pipes, because it relies on gravity for its flow, rather than pressure, while water supply is pressurized (B is correct, A is incorrect). Sanitary waste should not be mixed with storm drainage, because the sewage treatment plant is limited in capacity, and adding the storm drainage would completely overwhelm the plant (C is incorrect). Sanitary waste can be treated in cesspools or leach fields in remote sites, where no other treatment is available, although this is not a good solution in denser areas (D is incorrect).

25. **C.**   The pH scale ranges from 1 to 14. Readings of 1 to 6.9 are acidic, a pH of 7 is neutral, and a pH from 7.1 to 14 is alkaline. Therefore a pH of 12 would be highly alkaline (C is correct).

26. **C.**   The fixture trap, consisting of water standing in the U-shaped trap, was developed to block sewer gases from entering occupied spaces (choice B). As the fixture is used, however, the change in pressure within the pipe siphons the water out of the trap, rendering the trap ineffective. Therefore, the fixture vent was devised to equalize the pressure in the pipe. That is, air is drawn down the vent rather than water up from the trap, and this prevents siphoning of seal water out of the trap (correct choice C). Choices A and D are minor purposes incidental to the correct answer.

27. **B.**   A backflow preventer is a plumbing device installed between potable and nonpotable water systems, which allows flow from the potable to nonpotable, but not in the opposite direction. It often consists of two check valves in series (A) that allow the flow of fluid in only one direction. When the flow is reversed, the check valves are designed to close, thus preventing backflow. A gate valve (B) is a manually actuated shutoff valve, consisting of a sliding plate or gate that is perpendicular to the flow. Since it is not a backflow preventer, it is the correct answer to this question. A vacuum breaker (C) is an automatic valve that admits atmospheric air into a supply pipe upon a reverse in flow. This causes the flow to stop, preventing backflow and siphonage. Finally, an air gap fitting (D) is a device that separates two drain pipes with an unobstructed vertical air path to the atmosphere. This ensures that backflow will not take place in the event a sudden pressure loss and momentary vacuum occur.

28. **A, C, D, and E.**   The correct answers are copper, cement-lined cast iron,

plastic, and galvanized steel. Domestic water piping, which carries potable or drinking water, must be, most importantly, nontoxic. It must also be able to withstand high pressure, it must be easily connected with leakproof joints, and it must resist corrosion. One piping material that does not meet these requirements is lead. Lead is not only highly toxic, but it cannot withstand high pressure. Aluminum is also unable to withstand high pressure and is not used in water piping.

29. **C.**   The water that stays in a sanitary trap serves as a plug and keeps the methane gas from the sewers from rising into the building (C is correct). Arrestors are used to prevent shock and quiet plumbing systems (A is incorrect). Valves are used to stop the flow of water (B is incorrect). Stacks are vertical portions of a sanitary system, but do not prevent gasses from entering the building (D is incorrect).

30. **B.**   Interceptors are designed to prevent grease, hair, oil, etc., from getting into the sanitary system. They are required by code for certain establishments such as restaurants, which produce enough grease to create problems for the sewer system and treatment plant (B is correct). Traps are used to keep sewer gasses from entering the building (A is incorrect). Valves are used to stop the flow of water (C is incorrect). Cleanouts are a segment of pipe that allows a snake to be inserted into the sanitary line to remove clogs (D is incorrect).

31. **D.**   A pressure of 1 pound per square inch (psi) can lift a column of water 2.3 feet. Thus, 50 psi can lift water $50 \times 2.3 = 115$ feet (answer D). This is independent of the size of the pipe or column of water.

32. **C.**   100 psi − 15 psi for friction loss results in 85 psi at the building. In order to obtain 15 psi for the faucet, there can be a loss of no more than 70 psi (85 − 15 = 70 psi). 70 psi × 2.3 feet per psi = 161 feet. At 12 feet per story, the faucet may be located 13.4 floors above the ground. Therefore, the correct answer is 13 (C is correct).

33. **C.**   Latent heat is the heat transferred when there is a change of state, such as ice to water or water to vapor. Removing latent heat from the air (I) means removing water vapor from the air by changing it to water. However, the intake air is already lower in relative humidity than the comfort zone standards. If anything, moisture should be added to the intake air (III and correct choice C). Sensible heat is the heat that changes the temperature, but does not add moisture or change the state of a substance. Removing sensible heat would bring the dry bulb temperature within the comfort zone, but the RH would remain too low for comfort. Choice D is illogical, because it suggest that one can remove and add moisture to the air simultaneously to achieve a change in the level of comfort.

34. **D.**   The purpose of air filters is to prevent atmospheric dust, particles, and pollen from entering the HVAC system (correct answer D). As such, filters are generally placed where fresh air enters the heating, cooling, or humidifying equipment, so that it protects the equipment and promotes a more efficient operation. Air filters include both disposable and cleanable types, and the electrostatic type is a particularly effective air cleaner. Offensive odors (choice A) are not easily controlled with filters, although activated charcoal filters are sometimes used for this purpose.

Filters have no effect whatever on noise control (choice B), nor can they eliminate interior pollutants (choice C).

35. **C.** Convection, radiation, and conduction (choices A, B, and D) are the three heat transfer methods by which heat flows from hotter to colder surfaces of objects. Convection occurs in a fluid medium, such as air or water, and is the process that causes hot air to rise. Radiation transfers heat by electromagnetic waves, for example, the sun's rays that fall upon a surface. Conduction is the direct transfer of heat, such as the heat skin feels when you wash with hot water. These three methods of heat transfer occur without being affected by relative humidity. Latent heat (choice C) is the heat added to or removed from a substance when it changes state, for example the heat added to water (a liquid) when it becomes steam (a vapor). Latent heat is affected by humidity, and the greater the amount of moisture in the air, the greater the latent heat.

36. **A.** The return duct provides the means of recirculating (returning) the room air back to the supply fan, to be cooled or heated as required. Therefore A is correct.

37. **A.** Conduction is the method of transferring heat through a substance by passing from one particle to another. Convection is heat transfer by moving currents of air or any other gas or liquid. In a vacuum, there is no medium available to conduct heat or to create convection. We know, however, that heat transfers across a vacuum, because we receive heat from the sun across the vacuum of space. This method of heat transfer is radiation (correct answer A), which is the method of heat transfer in which heat travels rapidly in straight lines without heating the intervening space.

38. **D.** The body generates heat through metabolic action, and this heat is released through radiation, conduction, convection, and latent heat. The first three processes depend on the temperature of the environment. Latent heat transfer refers to the heat released by the evaporation of body moisture, through the lungs and through transpiration (sweating). The rate at which the moisture evaporates depends on how much moisture is already in the air, which is measured by the relative humidity. This is why relative humidity is so important on hot days, when the other mechanisms are not working, or may even be adding heat to the body. Then, the only mechanism able to remove heat is evaporation, which doesn't work very well if the humidity is too high.

39. **B.** The heating capacity of a plant is usually measured in Btuh, or Btu per hour, and the cooling capacity is measured in tons. The U-value is a measure of the insulating capacity of a wall, roof, or window assembly. The plant has to be sized to take care of the load generated by gain or loss through the walls and other internal loads. But the U-value is not a measure of the plant capacity.

40. **B, C, D, and E.** The correct answers are people, lighting, fixed equipment, and portable equipment. Cooling loads required for mechanical and electrical equipment must be taken into account and may be determined in one of several ways. Sometimes the Btuh is provided as part of the equipment specifications. In other cases, only the wattage or horsepower is available. In such cases, the Btuh may be calculated. Therefore, when performing

heating load calculations, heat generated by people, lighting, and fixed and portable equipment must be taken into account. Friction and prevailing winds do not usually affect the internal cooling of buildings.

41. A.   The amount by which the average outdoor temperature at a given location is below 65 degrees Fahrenheit for one day is called a degree day (A is correct). A design day is a day that is colder than 98 percent of the day's experienced in a given climate (B is incorrect).

42. C.   Air can hold more moisture when it is warm. If the air temperature drops below the temperature at which saturation occurs, the moisture will condense out. This results in either rain or dew. Thus, this temperature for a given moisture content is called the dew point temperature (C is correct).

43. C.   Evaporative coolers, also known as swamp or desert coolers, work by adding moisture to the air. A fan blows hot, dry outside air through pads that are kept moist by recirculated water. Although there is no change in the total heat content of the indoor air, relative humidity is increased and one feels cooler. It is the same principle as tying a wet kerchief around one's neck when working outside on a hot day. Because the greatest amount of moisture can be added to warm and dry air, evaporative cooling is most effective in a warm and dry climate, such as a desert (C is correct).

44. D.   One of the least efficient hydronic systems is the single pipe (choice A). With only one pipe, supply and return water are mixed after passing through the first coil, and this reduces the temperature of the water supply for the remaining coils

on the loop. A two-pipe system (choice B) is more efficient than a single-pipe system because there are separate supply and return pipes, which allows each coil to receive water at the same temperature. Both the single-pipe and two-pipe systems are limited to heating only. While a three-pipe system (choice C) is less expensive to install than a four-pipe system, operating expenses are greater. The three-pipe system allows simultaneous heating and cooling by means of separate pipes to the hot and cold coils. The disadvantage of the system is that hot and cold water are mixed in a single return pipe, producing water that is significantly different in temperature than the hot and cold return water leaving the coils prior to mixing. Therefore, the boiler and chiller consume more energy to heat or cool the water before it is pumped through the system again. The most versatile and energy efficient system is the four-pipe system (choice D), which allows simultaneous heating and cooling. With separate hot and cold water returns, the boiler and chiller require less energy than a three-pipe system to heat or chill the water.

45. A.   Evaporative coolers, sometimes referred to as swamp coolers or desert coolers, are quite appropriate in hot, arid climates (choice D is incorrect). They require a small amount of electricity to run a fan (choice B is incorrect) and a water supply to increase the relative humidity of the air supplied to a building (choice C is incorrect). By increasing the relative humidity of a space, occupants feel cooler, although there is no change in the total heat of the air (correct choice A). Most evaporative coolers are roof mounted, where large quantities of hot, dry outdoor air are blown through pads kept moist by recirculated water. The moist air is then delivered to the indoor space, where it cools the body and helps evaporation of body moisture. If a low relative humidity of 10 or 20 percent is raised to 50 percent, interior comfort improves dramatically. Evaporative coolers are quite effective in about half of the United States, from about the Midwest to the West Coast.

46. **D.**   Forced-air systems supply heated or cooled air efficiently by means of a fan and ductwork (choice A). By supplying more air than necessary, the building is positively pressurized, which eliminates infiltration (choice B). Supply ducts can be noisy, especially near the HVAC unit, where fan and air-velocity noises are the greatest. Therefore, supply ducts are insulated on the inside for sound control, and they are also generally insulated on the outside for temperature control (choice C). All forced-air systems require fresh outside air to be mixed with return air to maintain the optimum number of air changes. The outside air must always be heated or cooled, while the return air will be closer to the required temperature. The amount of outside air, however, should not be restricted simply because a harsh climate makes treating outside air more costly than in a more benign climate. Choice D is not a true statement and therefore the correct answer.

47. **C.**   A two-pipe system handles either hot water supply and return or chilled water supply and return. The single pump pumps the water either through a hot water boiler or a water chiller, depending upon which is required. Since only hot or chilled water is flowing, the building cannot be heated and cooled simultaneously. Therefore C is the only correct answer.

48. **D.**   An economizer is an energy-saving strategy in which a part of the HVAC system is shut off while the rest remains in operation. This system utilizes cool outside water or air to minimize cooling costs when outdoor temperatures are low (D is correct). The other devices listed are all part of the refrigeration cycle (A, B, and C incorrect).

49. **A.**   A variable air volume (VAV) with electric reheat is an HVAC system that accommodates thermal changes by varying the flow of supply air into a conditioned space. Providing an electric reheat allows the temperature of the air to be increased when needed at each mixing box, allowing the system to either heat or cool a given zone (A is correct).

50. **D.**   In comparison to the other choices listed, a round duct results in the least amount of friction loss due to the fact that the interior of a round duct has less surface area than a duct of another shape with the same cross-sectional area (D is correct).

51. **A.**   A device through which the air from a duct passes before entering a room is a diffuser (A is correct). Many diffusers contain adjustable veins that allow for the redirection of air. Grilles are openings in the ceiling where return or exhaust air usually leaves a room (B is incorrect). A turning vane is a device located within a duct that directs air around corners in ductwork (C is incorrect). A damper is a device that is located within a duct and allows for the control of the volume of air (D is incorrect).

52. **7,680 Btuh.**   The activity in a secretarial pool would be classified in the table as *Seated, light work, typing.* The maximum heat would be listed in the column *Total*

Heat, Adults, Male, showing a value of 640 Btuh. The correct answer is 12 people × 640 Btuh per person = 7,680 Btuh.

53. **0.0393.**   The U-value of an assembly is the reciprocal of the resistance. U = 1/R. 1/25.4 = 0.0393.

54. **60°F.**   Referring to the psychrometric chart, find where the 70 degree Fahrenheit vertical line intersects the 60 percent Rh curved line and follow the diagonal line upward and to the left to read the answer of 61 degrees Fahrenheit.

55. **B.**   Candidates are not expected to understand detailed circuiting requirements, however they should have an understanding of some of the more common devices used in electrical work. A common light switch with two positions, on and off, is called a two-way switch. When two light switches control the same fixture, each must be connected to the fixture and to each other—these are called three-way switches. Therefore 2 three-way switches are required for the situation given (B is correct). 2 two-way switches won't work since the switches cannot be connected to each other (A is incorrect). There is no such thing as a one-way switch (C is incorrect). Four-way switches allow many switches to create a continuous series of circuit connections and are used when three or more light switches control the same fixture.

56. **C.**   In an underground power district, the power company must provide service running underground to buildings. In overhead districts, they only need to provide service overhead. However, if a building owner in an overhead district desires underground service, the power company may elect to give him or her such service if the owner provides the underground conduit between the building and the power pole. The conduit needs to be encased in concrete only if the power is at a very high voltage. Therefore C is the correct answer.

57. **C.**   The flow of electricity is identified by Ohm's Law, which states that I = V/R, where I is the current, V is the potential, and R is resistance. Power is a measurement of work and is not a factor in the flow of electricity (C is correct).

58. **D.**   Transformers are called step up transformers when they increase the voltage and step down transformers when they decrease the voltage (D is correct). While a transformer changes the voltage in a circuit, it has practically no affect on the total power in the circuit.

59. **C.**   A three-phase electrical system has at least three wires and is identified by the voltage between any two of the wires, 480 volts being common. Sometimes a fourth wire, the neutral wire, is provided, which is normally grounded at the source for safety. The voltage between the neutral and any other wire is equal to the phase-to-phase voltage divided by 1.73. For example, where the phase-to-phase voltage is 480 volts, the phase-to-neutral voltage is 480 ÷ 1.73 = 277 volts. This system is then referred to as 480/277 volt three-phase power. The three-phase, four-wire system is very versatile; three-phase loads, such as motors and transformers, can be connected to the three-phase wires; and single-phase loads can be connected between any two-phase wires, or between any phase wire and the neutral wire, depending on the voltage rating of the load. Such systems can therefore serve all lighting and power needs, including motors. Answer C is therefore the best answer.

60. A and D. Since a VAV (variable air volume) system varies the volume, rather than the temperature, of supply air, at light loads the volume of air supplied will be reduced, thus reducing fan work and conserving fan energy. Therefore A is correct and B is incorrect. Since VAV systems are supplied from centralized fans, return air ducting is necessary (C is incorrect). As for future adaptability, adding zones to a VAV system merely requires tapping into the main supply duct with an additional VAV unit (D is correct). Since only the air volume is regulated by the VAV units and not the temperature, the system cannot supply heat and cooling to different areas simultaneously (E is incorrect). Finally, since each VAV unit has its own thermostat, temperature can be controlled in each zone separately.

61. A. Three-phase power is generated by putting three loops on the shaft and keeping them as separate circuits. If the loops are evenly spaced around the circumference of the shaft, the sine wave current generated is shifted by ⅓ of a cycle (or 120 degrees) between each circuit (A is correct).

62. B. Armored cable, which consists of a prewrapped set of wires encased in an interlocking metal spiral armor, is factory-assembled and may not be used underground or embedded in concrete (B is correct).

63. 10.9 ohms. To determine the resistance of the hair dryer, one must use Ohm's law, which states that the current (I) in amperes is directly proportional to the voltage (V) in volts and inversely proportional to the resistance (R) in ohms, or $I = V/R$. To solve for resistance, we rewrite the equation as $R = V/I$. Thus, R = 120 volts/11 amperes = 10.9 ohms.

64. 208 volts. $V1 = V2 \times \sqrt{3}$, therefore, 120 volts × 1.73 = 208 volts.

65. B. Luminance level refers to the amount of light without regard to its quality. Visual perception depends not only on the number of footcandles provided by a light source, but also on contrast, reflectance, and factors regarding the task, such as the importance of speed and accuracy. Nevertheless, empirical levels of desirable luminance have been established for various tasks, and the level recommended for routine office work is approximately 50 footcandles (correct choice B). This may be increased or decreased by 10 footcandles, depending on contrast levels, nature of the work, and even the worker's age. Incidentally, 30 footcandles would be suitable for rough assembly work, as in an auto factory, 70 footcandles for drafting rooms, and 150 footcandles for engraving work.

66. B. Answer A, the amount of light generated by a source, is the definition of intensity, which is represented by the letter I and measured in candlepower (cp). Luminance is the measure of how bright an object appears and is based on the reflectivity of a surface (choice C). Luminance is measured in footLamberts (fL). Choice D is the definition of a lumen, represented by the letter l. Illumination or illuminance, represented by the letter E, is the amount of light falling on a surface (choice B), and its value is expressed in footcandles (fc).

67. C. The CRI stands for the color rendering index, which measures how well light actually shows true color by comparing the source to daylight or an incandescent source at the same color temperature. CRI is often confused with color temperature itself, which defines whether the light is bluish or yellowish

(A is incorrect). The CRI is unrelated to energy efficiency (B), which is measured by the lamp efficacy, or the number of lumens the lamp generates per watt. The CRI is also independent of lamp life (D), although most lamps with better CRI tend to be less efficient and shorter lived.

68. A.   Shading coefficient (SC) is the ratio of solar heat gained through a window with shading devices in comparison to the solar heat gained by a single pane, clear glass window (A is correct).

69. B.   The retina is the sensing surface, the lens focuses, and the iris adjusts the amount of light (B is correct).

70. A.   The answer is *indirect*. In designing a computer lab, it is important to select a lighting system that minimizes glare or reflections in video display monitors. In this regard, the best lighting system is indirect lighting (choice A), without luminous bottoms or sides. In this system, light is aimed upward, where it reflects off ceiling and walls and produces an even lighting distribution without veiling reflections. Semi-indirect lighting (choice B) has 60 to 90 percent of the light directed upward, with the remaining light directed downward. This type of system has low direct or reflected glare. However, enough downward light remains to create distracting reflections in monitor screens. Semi-direct (choice C) is even less desirable, because only about 40 percent of the light is aimed upward towards the ceiling, resulting in greater glare. For most other situations, semi-direct lighting provides a pleasant working atmosphere and is often used in offices, classrooms, shops, and other such work areas. In a direct lighting system (choice D), common in many offices, the majority of light is directed downward. Ceilings and walls tend to appear dark because vertical surfaces are not illuminated. Although direct glare and veiling reflections for horizontal tasks can be controlled to some extent through appropriate design, it is impossible to eliminate the glare of fixtures reflected in computer monitors. Direct lighting, therefore, is the least appropriate choice for a computer lab space.

71. A.   Reflectors and refractors provide a specific distribution of light; that is, direct, indirect, focused, diffused, and so on. Although reduced glare and veiling reflections (reflected glare) may also be achieved with reflectors and refractors, that is not their primary purpose, and usually, the placement of the light source has a greater effect in this regard anyway. Increased visibility is generally accomplished by using additional light. Therefore A is the best answer.

72. B.   Lighting fixtures have a variety of light distribution patterns. Direct lighting fixtures (A) produce light which is undiffused and often glary. Indirect fixtures (B) produce highly diffused illumination, since the light is reflected off a surface that scatters it so that there is virtually no direct light. Semi-direct (C) and semi-indirect (D) fixtures have distribution patterns in between. Answer B is the best answer to this question.

73. B.   An incandescent lamp or bulb contains a filament, usually a tungsten alloy, which is heated by passing an electric current through it (B is correct). It glows, giving off light and a significant amount of heat.

74. B.   Translucent surfaces allow light to pass through, however, the light is also diffused prohibiting the transmission of the image (B is correct).

75. **58 fixtures.** The formula for the illumination in a room is:

E = (fixtures × lamps per fixture × lumens per lamp × maintenance factor × CU)/area.

Solving for the number of fixtures we get the following formula:

Fixtures = (area × E)/(lamps per fixture × lumens per lamp × maintenance factor × CU).

In this case:

Fixtures = (5,000 sf × 50 fc)/(3 lamps per fixture × 2,800 lumens per lamp × 0.8 × 0.65) = 57.23 fixtures, which we round up to 58 fixtures.

76. **A.** According to the inverse square law, the illumination at 20 feet is $(10/20)^2$ of that at 10 feet, or ¼ the value of the intensity at 10 feet. 12 fc/4 is 3 fc (correct answer A).

77. **C.** The answer is *104 fc*. Illuminance, which is the magnitude of illumination, is the intensity of luminous power expressed in lumens per unit area. One lumen per square foot, incidentally, is equal to one footcandle (fc). To determine illuminance, one uses the formula $E = 1\cos\theta/d^2$, where E is the illuminance on the receiving surface, I is the luminous intensity expressed in candlepower (cp), θ is the angle between a line perpendicular to the receiving surface and a line from the source to the surface, and d is the distance from the source to the surface. From the photometric chart, the intensity and 0 degrees is about one-third the distance between 1,500 cp and 2,000 cp, or 1,667 cp. The distance is four feet, and the angle θ is 0 degrees (the surface is directly

below the light, or perpendicular to the light beam). Therefore, $E = 1,667 \cos 0/4^2 = 104.2$ fc. The closest answer is C, which is 104 fc.

78. **A.** A sine wave represents a pure tone, such as that produced by an electronic instrument or a tuning fork. Most sounds, however, are not pure, but rather a complex combination of frequencies. Their waves, therefore, are irregular in shape (correct choice A). Sound intensity is inversely proportional to the square of the distance from the source (choice B). Since decibel levels are logarithmic, a 6-decibel increase represents a fourfold increase in sound level (choice C). Finally, the human ear can distinguish sounds between the frequencies of 20 and 20,000 hertz (Hz), but it is most sensitive to sounds in the middle frequencies (choice D), that is 125 to 6,000 Hz.

79. **A.** The answer is *a substantial reduction in noise, resulting in a comfortable office environment.* Sound intensity, or loudness, is measured in decibels (dB), where one decibel is defined as the least change in sound intensity that can be distinguished by the average human ear. The ratio between sound intensities is an approximate logarithmic ratio. Therefore, a reduction of 8 dB is a significant change, equivalent to about a 50 percent reduction in noise. An average office has a 50 dB rating, and therefore, the office described would have been noisy at 55 dB, but comfortable at 47 dB (choice A).

80. **A.** Good acoustics in a space allow the occupants to communicate and do their jobs without noise interference. One of the most important considerations in designing an acoustically comfortable space is reverberation, which is defined as the length of time it takes a sound

to die out after the source has stopped. Reverberation determines the live or dead qualities of a space, and different uses (C) have considerably different requirements. In a classroom with a dead quality, for example, sounds die out quickly, while in a church with a live quality, sounds reflect and persist, producing a richness to sermons and musical performances. Reverberation is based on several factors, including the volume of the space (B) and the absorption of the space's materials. The texture of a material (correct choice A), however, should not be equated with the material's absorption or likely acoustical performance. The type of noise to which a space is subjected (D) determines the frequency (Hz), location, and loudness (Db) of the noise one needs to control.

81. **B.**   Echoing (choice A) is caused when reflected sound reaches a listener more than 50 milliseconds after the original sound is heard, while flutter (choice C) consists of repeated echoes bouncing back and forth between two nonabsorbent parallel surfaces. The convergence of reflected sound paths is known as focusing (correct choice B), which is a condition often caused by concave surfaces, such as domes and vaults, or walls placed at certain angles. Diffusion (choice D) is the opposite of focusing and generally occurs when sound is reflected from convex surfaces. While some diffusion is desirable for musical performances, echoing, focusing, and flutter are considered undesirable.

82. **A.**   The loudness of sound depends not only on intensity, but also on the frequency of the sound and characteristics of the human ear. The range of intensity to which the ear responds is enormous; a very loud sound can develop two and one half trillion times the intensity of a barely audible sound. Sound intensity is measured in decibels, and the ratio between two sounds has an approximate logarithmic relation. Because of this logarithmic relationship, 40 decibels is not twice as loud as 20 decibels; it is actually more like 100 times as loud. As far as the office in our question is concerned, an eight decibel reduction—from 70 db to 62 db—is approximately a 50 percent reduction in the noise level (correct answer A).

83. **B.**   Effective acoustical design considers the total problem, not just cosmetic surface treatments. Beyond acoustical tile on the ceiling or carpeting on the floor, good design involves the type of construction to control sound transmission, as well as the shape of a space to control reverberation. Perfect geometrical shapes, such as circular plans or cubic spaces for example, are configurations that can lead to acoustical "hot spots," or repeated reflections of sound. This sort of reverberation is almost always objectionable and, therefore, should be avoided (A). The sound that strikes concave wall surfaces is also difficult to control; however, convex surfaces are highly desirable, because they diffuse sound very effectively (incorrect statement and correct answer B). Regarding statements C and D, reverberation is greatly affected by the size of a space. When the time interval between a sound and its reflection is too short, a true echo cannot be distinguished, and that is why no echoes are possible in a very small room. On the other hand, in very large spaces, such as some cathedrals and train stations, the reverberation time has been found to be as long as 30 seconds.

84. B.   Sound travels at a speed of about 1,130 feet per second. If the walls and ceiling of a room are not absorbent, that is to say, if they are not covered with sound-absorbing draperies or porous materials, the sound will not just reflect once from each wall, but will bounce from wall to wall, passing by the listener's ear many times in a second and creating many modes of vibration in the room. Obviously, the sound loses some energy at the walls and while traveling through the air, and thus, the level of the sound decreases each time it is reflected and crosses the room. In acoustics, this is known as reverberation, and reverberation time is defined as the number of seconds it takes for the sound to fade below hearing level. Ideally, the reverberation time of a concert hall should be adjusted to suit the style of music being performed. Most modern halls, however, serve a wide variety of music, and the architect must therefore seek the best compromise. Acceptable median reverberation times range from 1.5 seconds to 2.0 seconds (correct answer B). Shorter reverberation times produce a dry and lifeless sound, whereas longer periods produce overlapping sounds that lack clarity and definition and sound blurred or muddy. A reverberation time of zero, choice A, is unrealistic and generally unattainable; five to ten seconds, choices C and D, is extremely long, and results in very poor acoustics.

85. B.   In large commercial buildings, building automation systems are often used to control automatic equipment to assure proper operation of the facility. HVAC systems, fire detection and alarm systems, and elevators are several of the systems commonly controlled by such equipment. Drinking fountains are typically self-contained units and typically are not controlled by automation equipment (B is correct).

86. C.   Hubs and switches are network devices that are used as centralized points in a wired network. These devices control, manage, and direct communications traffic through that segment of the network connected through that device (A and B are incorrect). A patch panel is a device that allows a temporary and flexible connection between two systems or subsystems. In data communications the patch panel is normally located in the telecommunications room or closet and care must be taken in the provision of space and location of these items (D is incorrect). A panelboard is a component of an electrical distribution system, not a data network (C is correct).

87. A, C, E, and F.   The correct answers are height of the building, weight of building equipment, number of occupants at the highest floor, and building function and schedule. The height of a building (A) affects the rated speed of elevators, and the number of occupants on the highest floor as well as other floors (E) determines the cab platform size and total number of cars required. Less obvious is the need to provide vertical transportation for large or heavy items, such as large furnishings, power transformers (C), and other equipment. Freight elevator service may be provided by a separate car or by using a passenger car during off hours, but in any event, the capacity of the cab is determined by the heaviest item that might reasonably be moved. The location of standpipes (B) and emergency evacuation standards (D) have no influence on the number of elevators required. Elevators are never permitted to be used as fire evacuation routes, and in the event of an emergency, most elevators are programmed to return to the building lobby. Finally, building functions and schedule (F) should be considered to determine whether elevator use will occur at certain peak times, or be evenly distributed throughout the day.

88. **C.** This question could be deceptive if you are not entirely clear on the meaning of the terms used or how maximum traffic and capacity are determined. To begin with, both statements A and B are partially correct and deal with elevator traffic, which is computed on the basis of the number of passengers carried during a five minute span. Traffic is figured for peak or critical traffic periods, which vary considerably with the type and use of the building. For example, office buildings usually reach their maximum peak during lunch time (B), but hospitals might reach their maximum peak during visiting hours, and hotels reach theirs in the morning, early evening, and at check-out time (A). Elevator capacity, on the other hand, is based simply on car size (correct answer C), that is, the number of people an elevator car will comfortably hold. Travel speed (D) is considered only when computing elevator traffic-handling capacity, which requires both car size (the number of people carried) and round trip time, which is based on speed. In other words, capacity, which represents the number of people per car, and handling capacity, which represents the number of people carried during a five minute span, are two entirely different concepts.

89. **B.** The candidate must first know that in a highrise office building, transporting people as fast as possible is one of the primary considerations in ensuring that the structure functions properly. The electric passenger elevator operates at the highest rate of speed of those given, and therefore is most suitable for transporting people in highrise office buildings. Their speed can be as high as up to 1,800 feet per minute (B is correct). The other types of equipment listed operates at much lower speeds: the escalator, which operates at two standard speeds, 90 fpm and 120 fpm, and the hydraulic passenger elevator, which is the slowest since its travel distance rarely exceeds 50 feet (A and D are incorrect). Further, it should be understood that the heavy lifting capability of freight elevators makes them slower than passenger elevators and unsuitable for transporting building occupants (C is incorrect).

90. **B.** Hydraulic elevators are operated by an oil driven ram from below and are commonly used for lowrise buildings up to about 50 feet. These elevators have speeds that vary between 25 and 150 feet per minute. Because of their short travel distance at relatively low speeds, hydraulic elevators are commonly used for passengers in garden apartments, motels, and other similar buildings (B is correct). Electric elevators operate at much higher speeds (up to 1,800 fpm) and are lifted by cables from above. They are typically used in high-rise construction (A is incorrect). Escalators operate in the approximate speed range given (90 to 120 fpm) but are not ram-driven and can serve only one story each (C is incorrect).

91. **C.** The answer is *wet-pipe*. Preaction systems (choice A) feature an early alarm, which is activated when water fills the pipes but before the sprinklers discharge. This is especially useful where a building's contents are subject to water damage, such as computer rooms, since the early alarm often permits the fire

to be extinguished manually before the sprinklers open. Deluge systems (choice B) are used where rapid fire spread is anticipated, such as in garages or aircraft hangers. In deluge systems all sprinkler heads discharge at once. In the most common wet-pipe systems (choice C) water is always under pressure throughout all pipes. Sprinklers in the area affected are opened by heat-sensitive elements in the sprinkler heads themselves. Finally dry-pipe systems (choice D) have pipes filled with compressed air until the opening of a sprinkler head permits water flow.

92. **B.** The answer is *III only.* The four classes of fires are as follows: Class A involves ordinary materials such as wood and paper, Class B involves flammable liquids such as gases and oils, Class C is electrical fires, and Class D involves combustible metals such as sodium and magnesium. Halon is a gas that is used in both hand-held and automatic extinguishing systems to suppress all classes of fires, with the exception of Class D fires (I is incorrect). Halon is nontoxic, when used at normal concentrations, and especially advantageous for fires involving expensive contents, because it leaves no residue and does not damage valuable equipment or documents (III). Fire suppression systems that use carbon dioxide (CO_2) displace room oxygen to smother a fire. When the carbon dioxide dissipates, it is possible for smoldering embers to reignite (II is incorrect). CO_2 systems require that occupants leave the area (IV is incorrect), thus requiring audible and visible alarms to warn people about the presence of toxic fumes. Since only statement III is true, B is the correct answer.

93. **B.** Class B fires involve flammable gases and liquids, such as gasoline or propane. Class A fires involve ordinary materials, such as wood, paper, cloth, and rubber. Class C fires are electrical fires. Class D fires involve combustible metals, such as sodium, potassium, or magnesium. It is difficult or even dangerous to try to fight Class B, C, or D fires with water, and other fire-fighting methods must be provided.

94. **D.** Carbon monoxide is a byproduct of combustion and is not used in firefighting (D is correct). Halon and carbon dioxide are used as special extinguishing media and are used where water would damage sensitive equipment or materials, such as in computer centers or museums.

95. **B.** *Supply dampers in the fire area must be fully closed* (B is correct). In this technique of smoke control, upon the detection of fire, exhaust dampers in the fire area change to fully open and exhaust fans increase their speed in order to draw smoke out of the building (A and D are incorrect). Conversely, supply dampers are closed and fans shut down to avoid supplying fresh air and oxygen to the fire (C is incorrect).

96. **10.0.** In order to answer this question, a candidate must understand the terminology: U, K, and R. The U-factor is the overall coefficient of heat transfer of a building section (floor, roof, or wall), and is equal to the number of Btu per hour that will pass through one square foot of the section when the temperature difference is 1°F. Thus, the lower the U-value, the less heat transferred, and therefore, the better its insulation characteristics. The K-factor is the coefficient of heat transfer of a material exactly one inch thick, and is

equal to the number of Btu per hour that will pass through one square foot of the material per inch of thickness when the temperature difference is 1°F. The lower the K-value, the less heat transferred, and thus the better the insulation properties of the material. R is the resistance to heat transfer of a material or a building section. When referring to a material, R is the reciprocal of K (R = 1/K), and when referring to an overall building section, R is the reciprocal of U (R = 1/U). The greater the R-value, the less heat transferred, and therefore the better the insulating properties of the material or the section. The original U-value of the wall is 0.20. Since R = 1/U, R = 1/0.20 = 5.0. Now we add 1½ inches of insulation having a K-value of 0.30. R for the insulation is equal to 1/K 1/0.30 = 3.33 per inch of thickness. Since the insulation is 1½ inches thick, its total resistance R = 1.5 × 3.33 = 5.0. The total R for the wall plus the 1½ inches of added insulation is 5.0 + 5.0 = 10.0. The combined U-factor is 1/total R = 1/10.0 = 0.10.

97. **C.**   Candidates are expected to have a general understanding of the cost of construction. For an office building, a reasonable estimate of the cost of the building's mechanical and electrical systems would be approximately 30 percent of the total construction cost. If the building is 50,000 square feet and costs $120.00/square foot, this results in an overall construction cost of $6,000,000. 30 percent of this figure equates to $1,800,000 (correct answer is C).

98. **26 ft.**   Residential codes typically require that chimneys and fireplaces terminate two feet above the roof and two feet above any part of the building within ten feet. 24 ft. + 2 ft. = 26 ft.

99. **135 square feet.**   Central heating furnaces not listed for alcove or closet installation shall be installed in a room or space having a volume at least 12 times that of the furnace. The volume of the furnace is 3' × 6' × 5' = 90 cubic feet. Multiply 90 cubic feet by 12 to get the required room volume: 90 × 12 = 1,080 cubic feet. The room's ceiling height is 8 feet, so 1,080 cubic feet divided by 8 feet leaves a room area of 135 sq. ft.

100. **A, C, D, and E.**   The factors presently used to evaluate "life cycle costs" are the first costs, the operating and maintenance costs, periodic replacement costs and the residual value of the design element—all easily identifiable costs.
"Life Cycle Assessment," "Cradle to Cradle," and "Embedded Energy" analysis also include factors more difficult to price. These include the cost of the energy used to transport products and the cost to the environment after the product is no longer viable.

101. **A, B, C, and E.**   LEED covers a range of architectural decisions, including site design, water usage, energy conservation and production, indoor air quality, building materials, natural lighting, views of the outdoors, and innovative design components. It does not cover psychological or behavioral affects or design styles.

102. **A, B, D, and F.**   Light Colored Roofing materials reflect sunlight and reduce the amount of radiation that is absorbed through the roof into the interior space—a passive solar design strategy. Dark colored roofing increases the interior heat load. Roof Ponds or vegetated roof areas also have good insulating value and reduce the urban heat island effect and provide cooling through evapotranspiration. The

remaining categories describe effective passive solar design strategies.

103. **A, C, D, and E.** Light shelves permit daylight to reflect off the ceiling and penetrate further into the interior. LED lighting lasts longer than incandescent and is less expensive to operate. High Efficiency Light Fixtures and those with dimming and multiple switching capability require less energy to operate. These are all sustainable lighting practices.
Energy efficient fixtures produce more—not fewer—lumens per watt. Bubble skylights allow heat gain from the south, unlike sawtooth skylights which only allow the glass to face north, blocking heat gain.

104. **53.3 psi.** A 9-story building has 8 floor plates. Total lift = 8 floor plates × 11 ft. / story = 88 feet
Since 2.3 feet is equivalent to 1 psi, 88 feet is equivalent to 88/2.3 = 38.3 psi
Required water pressure = 38.3 psi for lift + 15 psi for flush = 53.3 psi

105. **A, C, and D.** Galvanized steel, copper tubing and PVC plastic pipe are all in general use today. Black iron was the term for untreated steel pipe used in the past which was very susceptible to rust and corrosion and was replaced by galvanized steel. ABS pipes are another type of plastic pipes and are not made from zinc.

106. **A, C, D, and E.** Gate, globe, check, and angle valves are used in standard plumbing systems. An access valve is not an actual valve type. Water hammer refers to a thumping or rattling sound that occurs when a faucet is shut off rapidly and requires a cushioning or damping device.

107. **B, C, and D.** Acidic water causes corrosion, not deposition. Plastic pipe, including PVC, should never be used in exposed locations above ground because it deteriorates when exposed to ultra-violet light, which is present in direct sunlight. Where water is acidic, corrosion-resistant materials like copper and PVC are appropriate for piping. Plastic pipe does not corrode and does not allow the electrolysis that deposits mineral ions. The zeolite process controls hardness—not acidity.

108. **A, B, and D.** Convection occurs only in a fluid medium like air or liquid. Water is the only material that expands when it gets colder, and only just before it freezes. Convection occurs in rooms all the time, especially in large atrium spaces as well as inside wall cavities. Convection is the only means of heat transfer that is strictly directional, and can transfer heat both upwards and horizontally—never downwards.

109. **A, B, D, and F.** The CLTD (Cooling Load Temperature Differential) is based on wall mass, orientation and color, which relate to conduction and radiation.

110. **B and C.** A constant amount of water in the air does not represent a constant relative humidity (RH). Relative humidity is defined as the percentage of complete saturation (how much water is in the air at a given temperature compared to how much the air could hold at that temperature). Air can hold much more water when it is warm than when it is cold. However, we always put a vapor barrier on the warm side of the insulation in a wall. In the United States, for people doing sedentary work who are lightly clothed, the Comfort Zone ranges from about 25% to 75% RH. Moving air shifts the comfort zone to slightly higher temperatures (that is why we are more comfortable in front of a fan even though the temperature and RH have not changes).

111. A, C, D, and E.   A flat plate collector is a flat surface tilted at the right ALT and AZ angles to receive most of the sun's rays as directly as possible. A bent Fresnel lens is used to focus the incoming sunlight and uses less material than a normal lens. Photovoltaic cells directly generate electricity from the sunlight by creating an electrical charge when they are exposed to light. The most common cheap cell now is an amorphous silicon cell, often found on "solar" calculators. All of these are components of Active Solar Systems. Trombe walls and nighttime flushing systems are used in Passive Solar Systems.

112. B, C, and D.   The correct answers are altitude angle, azimuth angle, and intensity of the sun. The declination angle is affected only by the time of year, not the time of day. Speed of transit is constant.

113. C, D, and E.   The following statements are true:
Evaporation goes on at a very low temperature and absorbs heat from its surroundings. The evaporative chiller is often called a cooling tower. In seasons when it is cool enough outside, the outside air may be used directly and the refrigeration cycle shut off.
However, Freon is circulated in a closed loop—not an open loop. The pressure in the loop causes changes in temperature, evaporation AND in condensation. Cool water from clean ponds may be used in early winter and late spring instead of chilled refrigerant water.

114. A, B, and D.   Electrical Systems comprise one of the three basic categories. They are justified only in very mild climates where the system is off most of the time, since this is generally the most expensive system distribution type in terms of life-cycle costs. Radiant Systems typically fall within this category. Two-, three-, and four-pipe systems are different loop patterns in the piping of Hydronic Systems. The third basic category in Distribution Systems for Mechanical Equipment consists of Forced Air Systems.

115. A, D, and F.   The three correct statements:
Forced air systems distribute heated or cooled air around the building using supply ducts. Fans must be isolated from the floor on which they sit and from the ducts to which they are attached so their vibrations are not transmitted as noise throughout the building. And the most common forced air system is the VAV system.
Regarding the incorrect statements:
Fresh air intakes should be located away from both the cooling tower and other exhausts. To positively pressurize a building the supply fan needs to be run at a rate HIGHER than the sum of return air and the leakage rate. In a fan coil system, a constant volume of cleaned and conditioned air can heat and cool simultaneously but is supplied from the plant in a SINGLE duct.

116. 24,000 Btuh.   A ton of cooling is equivalent to 12,000 Btuh, which is the rate of heat transfer that would melt one ton of ice over a 24-hour period. It would require 24,000 Btuh to melt two tons of ice over a 24-hour period.
2 tons × 12,000 Btuh = 24,000 Btuh

117. 12 inches of static head.   One inch of static head is the pressure required to support a one inch column of water. Therefore, 12 inches of static head are required to support a 12 inch column of water.

118. 3 amps.   The general equation for power in a DC circuit is P = V × I
Where
P = power in watts
V = voltage
I = the current in amps
R = resistance in ohms
I = V / R = 12v / 4 ohms = 3 amps
P = V × I = 12v × 3 amps = 36 watts

119. A, B, and F.   Transformers are called step up transformers when they increase the voltage and step down transformers when they decrease the voltage. They waste surprisingly little energy, but what is wasted turns into heat, which must be dissipated by the transformer. Transformers must be properly ventilated, since their thermal rating is based on the assumption that the surrounding air will be able to remove heat at a certain rate from their cooling fins. If a large transformer overheats, it may explode. The fluid that insulates the electricity and cools the transformer is often toxic, and the explosion my vaporize it or spray it over adjacent surroundings or people (the reason they are located outside or within a fireproof vault.) The remaining three statements are correct.

120. A, C, D, and E.   Of the four types of motors in general use, the DC Motor is used for small scale applications and for elevators. The Single-Phase AC Motor are used in many sizes and shapes, typically ¾ horsepower or less. Large motors are typically Three-Phase Induction Motors. Universal Motors run on either AC or DC current and are often found in mixers, hand drills and similar appliances. Thermal Relays are not motors but protect motors from overload. Wye refers to an electrical connection.

121. A, C, and F.   Correct Load Estimating Factors:
Lighting Load (estimate 2-5 watts/sf)
Convenience Outlet Load (estimate 1-3 watts/sf)
HVAC Load (estimate 4-7 watts/sf)
In addition, it is wise to include 0.2-0.7 watts/sf for Miscellaneous Uses

122. 100 amps.   The minimum electrical service for a residence is now 100 amps.

123. 1.0 ohms.
$R = 1 / (1R1 + 1/R2 + 1/R3)$
$= 1 / (1/4 + 1/4 + 1/2)$
$= 1 / 1$
$= 1.0$ ohm

124. 208v.
$V_2 = V_1$ / square root of 3
$V_1 = V_2$ × square root of 3 = 120v × 1.73 = 208v

125. 1.   If we drew a one square foot square in midair, at a distance of one foot from a one candlepower source, the amount of light flowing through that square would be termed one lumen.

126. 18.75 fc.   If the source of light may be approximated as a point (candle, light bulb, even a single tube or fluorescent fixture), the flux, and resultant illumination, is inversely proportional to the square of the distance from the surface.
$E = I$ (intensity) / d squared
$= 1,200$ fc / (8 ft) x (8 ft)
$= 1,200$ fc / 64
$= 18.75$ fc

127. 6 fc.   Doubling the distance to a surface cuts the illumination to one quarter.
24 fc × ¼ = 6 fc

128. A, B, and D.   The first two statements are correct. Cool white—not warm white—produces the most lumens per watt. Fluorescent lighting does not run on 12 volt DC current. The lifetime of a fluorescent is determined both by the number of hours it is lit and also by the number of times it is switched on and off, which tends to wear it out. Mercury vapor fixtures are not fluorescent fixtures, but are High Intensity Discharge (HID) lamps.

129. 72 fc.   If there were 1,800 fc on the ground outside, then a DF of 4 would result in an illumination level of 1,800 fc × 0.04 = 72 fc.

130. 68 dB.   The co-worker sits 60 feet away from the sound source (15 ft. + 45 ft. = 60 ft.). The IL at 15 feet from the sound source is 80 dB. The IL at 30 feet (2 × 15 ft. = 30 ft.) is 6 dB less than at 15 feet (80 dB − 6 dB = 74 dB). The IL at 60 feet (2 × 30 ft. = 60 ft.) is 6 dB less than at 30 feet (74 dB − 6 dB = 68 dB).
This results in a decibel level of 68 dB for the co-worker.

131. 3 dB.   Doubling the source power results in an increase of 3 dB.

132. 153 sabins.
A = 12 × 15 × .60 (floor with carpet).
  2 × 12 × 10 × .07 (two 12 ft. gyp bd walls)
  2 × 15 × 10 × .07 (two 15 ft. gyp bd walls)
  12 × 15 × .04 (plaster ceiling)
  = 108 + 16.8 + 21 + 7.2
A = 153 absorptivity in sabins

133. .57 seconds.
T_R = .049 V/A
  T_R = reverberation time in seconds
  V = volume of the space in cubic feet
  A = total absorptivity in sabins
T_R = .049 × (12 × 15 × 10) / 153 sabins
  .049 × 1,800 cubic feet / 153 sabins
  .576 seconds

134. 24 feet.   The maximum slope permitted for a handicapped ramp is 1:12. Thus, if the difference of elevation is 2 feet, then the length of the ramp must be at least 12 × 12 feet, or 24 feet.

135. B, C, D, and E.   The first and last statements apply to Hydraulic Elevators which are commonly used for lowrise buildings (about 50 feet or five stories maximum.)

136. 926 feet per minute.   As a rule of thumb, the rated elevator speed may be figured as 1.6 times the rise in feet, plus 350.
360 feet × 1.6 = 576 + 350 = 926 feet per minute

137. 30 degrees.   The normal angle of incline is approximately 30 degrees and the operating speed is either 90 fpm or 120 fpm along the incline.

138. 44 inches.   120 × 0.2 = 24 inches. However, the minimum width of any part of an exit passage cannot be less than 44 inches wide.

Notes

Notes